Cat and Girl

VOLUME III

by Dorothy Gambrell

"Do we **look** like we're progressing?"

Freedom of Choice

CHANNEL 501.
WRESTLING.
CLICK
CHANNEL 502.
SHARK WEEK.
CLICK
CHANNEL-
I MISS BROADCAST TELEVISION.
CLICK
THE FICTION THAT WE ALL WANT TO WATCH THE SAME THING.
CHANNEL 503.
COCKFIGHTING.
COCKFIGHTING?!
IT'S MORE EXCITING THAN BUNNY FIGHTING.
CLICK CLICK
CHANNEL 505.
THE CONSENSUS IS GONE.
THE WRITERS ARE GONE.
ULTIMATE SHARK FIGHTING CHAMPIONSHIP.
CLICK CLICK CLICK
THE PROFESSIONALS HAVE LEFT THE BUILDING.
FOLK CULTURE HAS TURNED MASS CULTURE HAS TURNED FOLK CULTURE ONCE MORE.
NUTS TO THIS.
WHAT'S ON YOUTUBE?

Rods and Cones

POKE
OW!
POKE
THE WATER'S BEEN TURNED OFF.
THE GAS IS OFF.
OW! GEEZ.
WE HAVE TO FIND A WAY TO SAVE MONEY!
WELL YOU CAN STOP PAYING FOR COLOR ON THE TELEVISION BECAUSE I AM GONNA POKE MYSELF IN THE EYE UNTIL I CAN'T SEE NOTHING BUT THE BLUES!
WE DON'T
ALL THE GREATS DID IT!
YOU DON'T
STEVIE WONDER!
RAY CHARLES!
DOC WATSON!
MOONDOG.
COLORBLIND BLAKE.
COLORBLIND WILLIE McTELL.
I DON'T THINK YOU CAN MAKE YOURSELF COLORBLIND.
I DON'T CRUSH YOUR DREAMS.

Surround Sound

TZZZP
LIFE IS DIFFICULT ENOUGH WITHOUT DIFFICULT MUSIC.

Organization

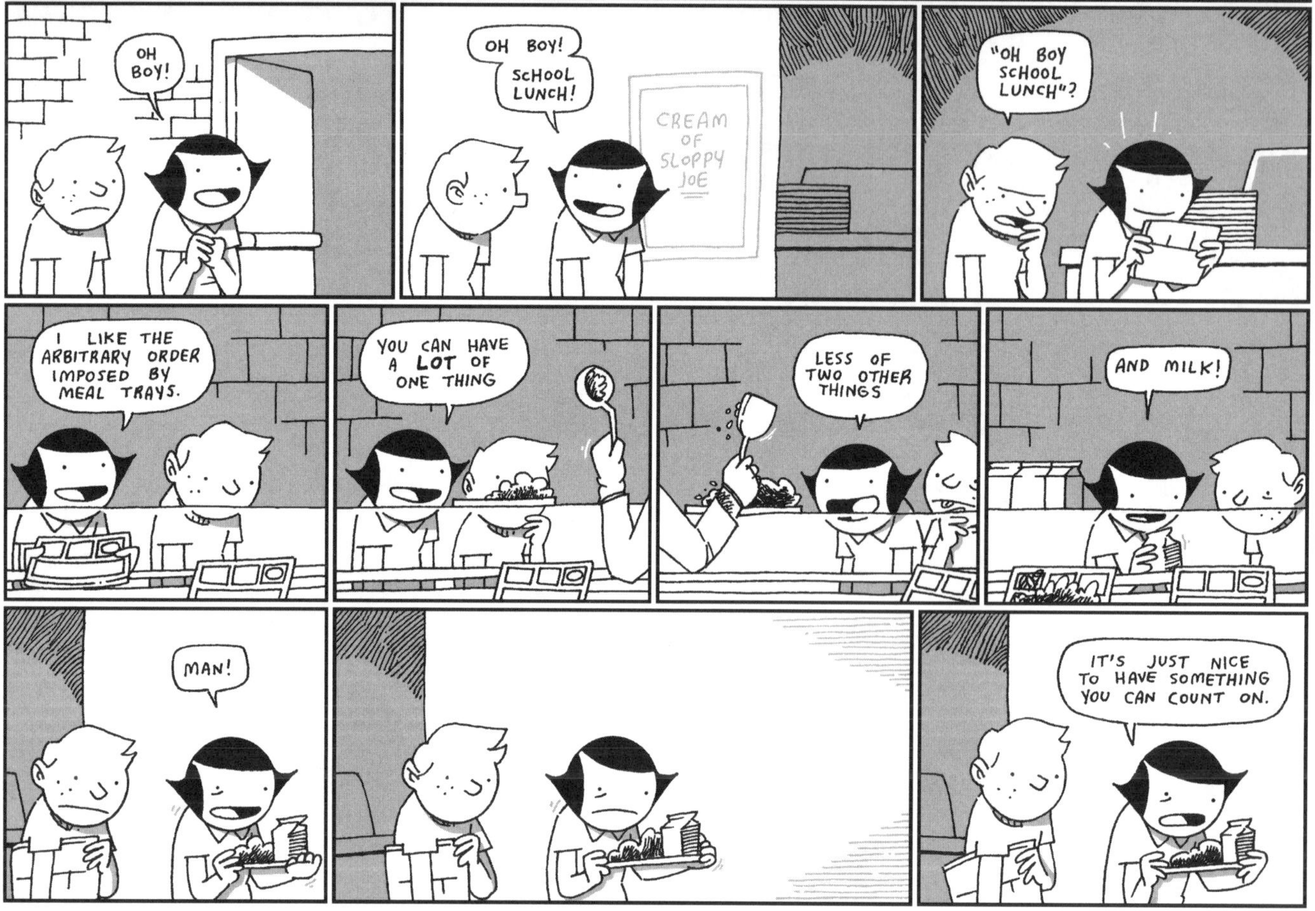
OH BOY!
OH BOY! SCHOOL LUNCH!
CREAM OF SLOPPY JOE
"OH BOY SCHOOL LUNCH"?
I LIKE THE ARBITRARY ORDER IMPOSED BY MEAL TRAYS.
YOU CAN HAVE A **LOT** OF ONE THING
LESS OF TWO OTHER THINGS
AND MILK!
MAN!
IT'S JUST NICE TO HAVE SOMETHING YOU CAN COUNT ON.

Steak House

$
I'LL HAVE A GLASS OF WATER AND A PLATE OF PARSLEY.
AND I WILL HAVE YOUR MOST EXPENSIVE SLAB OF MEAT PRODUCT.
HOW WOULD YOU LIKE THAT?
VERY WELL-DONE LIKE
ACHEWOOD
OR RARE
LIKE A SYMPATHETIC FEMALE CHARACTER IN ACHEWOOD.
BUT-
EVERYONE KNOWS MOLLY IS JUST A PROP FOR ROAST BEEF.

Dietary Restrictions

I CAN'T DRINK MILK.
I WON'T EAT BEEF OR PORK.
IS THAT FREE RANGE?
I DON'T DO PROCESSED FOODS.
I ONLY EAT ANIMALS WHOSE MORALS I FIND PERSONALLY REPULSIVE.
I DON'T DRINK TAP WATER.
I CAN'T DRINK SODA.
I WILL **ONLY** DRINK SODA.
DO YOU HAVE COFFEE?
DOES THAT HAVE RIBOFLAVIN?
I'M SORT OF ALLERGIC TO RIBOFLAVIN.
I REFUSE TO ORDER ANY SANDWICH WITH A CLEVER NAME.

Casual Fans

WHAT'S YOUR TEAM?
THE BRONCOS.
YOU'RE FROM DENVER?
I LIKE JOHN DENVER.
YOU?
THE DALLAS COWBOYS!
BECAUSE YOU LIKE COWBOYS.
BECAUSE I LOVE "STELLA DALLAS."
I LIKE THE BEARS.
IF I COULD JUST ROOT FOR BARBARA STANWYCK-
AREN'T THE BEARS OWNED BY JUDY CHICAGO?
THERE ARE SO MANY WAYS TO BE WRONG IN THIS WORLD.

Entertainment

WHAT DID PEOPLE DO BEFORE TELEVISION?
I DON'T KNOW.
I GUESS AFTER DINNER THEY SAT AROUND AND STARED AT THE WALL.
DID THE WALL HAVE COMMERCIALS?
NO.
NOT BAD.

True Confessions

I ACCIDENTALLY LIKED A RADIOHEAD SONG.

Exile

PARTY! FORTY DAYS!
IT'S FORTY DAYS IN THE DESERT!
GLUG GLUG GLUG
AH
IF THE GOOD LORD DIDN'T MEAN FOR US TO DRINK IT HE WOULDN'T HAVE MADE IT WET.
WHAT DO YOU THINK BROUGHT MOSES HERE?
HE GOT PRICED OUT OF EGYPT.

SSSSsIp
FFFFFFFF
CHK CHK CHK CHK
SPLOOSH
IT WAS JUST ICE!

Why I Live at the A&P

SISYPHUS.
JEANNIE.
JOE MEEK.
LOTS OF PEOPLE HAVE TROUBLE WITH THEIR LANDLORD.
NOW-
NOW A SEALORD-
A SEALORD MIGHT BE KIND OF COOL.
EVEN POSEIDON DOES A CREDIT CHECK!

Oasis

BOTTLED WATER.
PEOPLE MAKE AN AWFUL LOT OF MONEY SELLING BOTTLED WATER!
PEOPLE MAKE MONEY AT JOBS WHERE THEY SIT AT DESKS TOO.
BUT NO ONE IS BOTTLING THE OTHER ELEMENTS.
FIRE?
WELL YOU'D HAVE TO DEVELOP A SPECIAL BOTTLE FOR FIRE
BUT YOU COULD START ON WIND AND EARTH RIGHT AWAY.
WHO IS GOING TO BUY BOTTLED EARTH?
PEOPLE AT THE BEACH.
JOGGERS.

Nothing Left to Lose

THERE IS A FREEDOM IN NOT HAVING MONEY.
I READ THAT IN A BOOK ONCE.
IS THERE FREEDOM IN NOT EATING BREAKFAST?
FOOD FOR CAT
I GUESS THERE MUST BE.
FREEDOM FEELS LIKE MY EYES DON'T FOCUS ANYMORE.
FOOD FOR
FOOD FOR CAT
WHO WOULD WIN IN A FIGHT
BOOKS OR LIVED EXPERIENCE?
LIVED EXPERIENCE FIGHTS DIRTY.

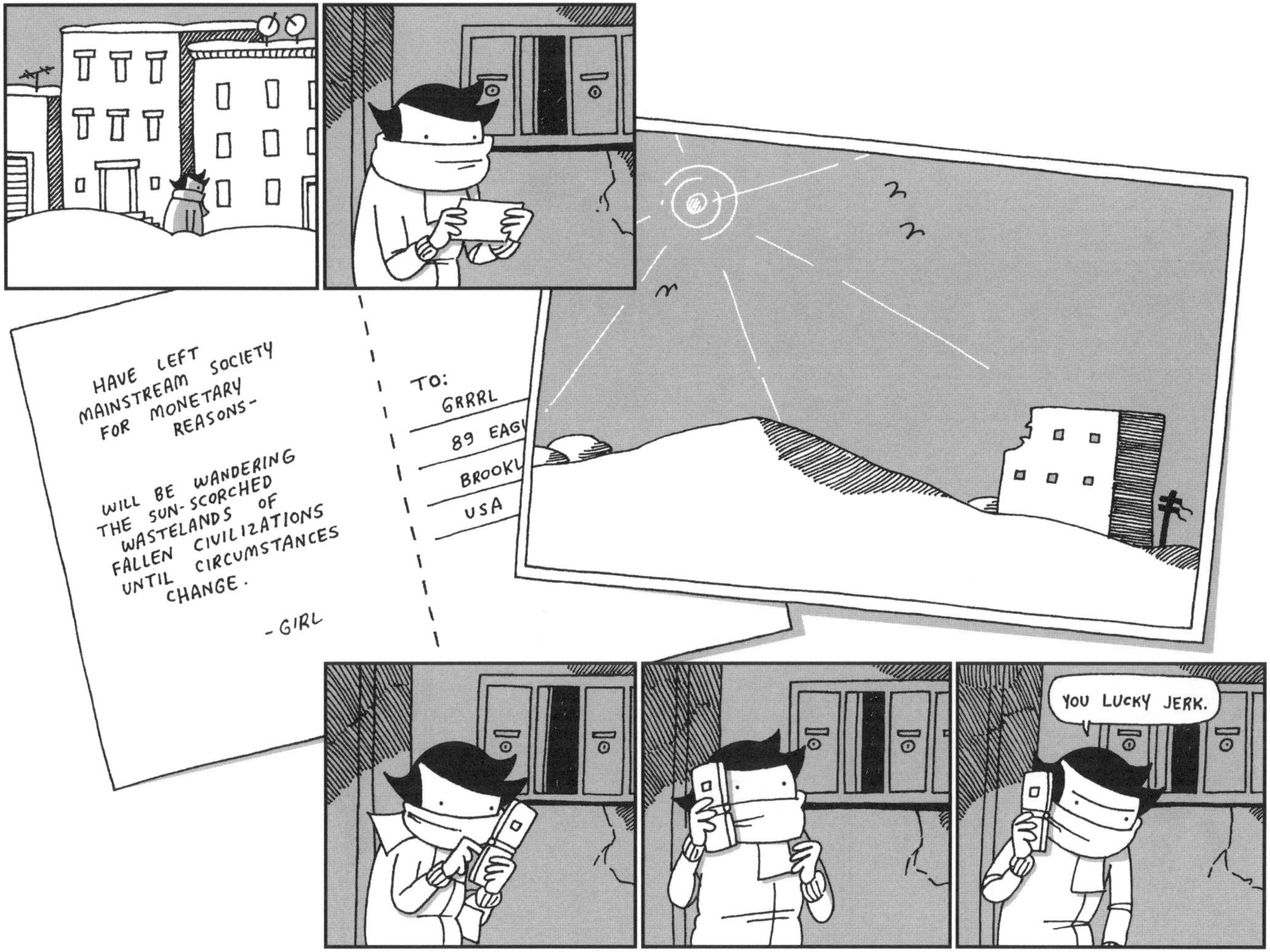
HAVE LEFT MAINSTREAM SOCIETY FOR MONETARY REASONS-
WILL BE WANDERING THE SUN-SCORCHED WASTELANDS OF FALLEN CIVILIZATIONS UNTIL CIRCUMSTANCES CHANGE.
-GIRL
TO:
GRRRL
89 EAG
BROOK
USA
YOU LUCKY JERK.

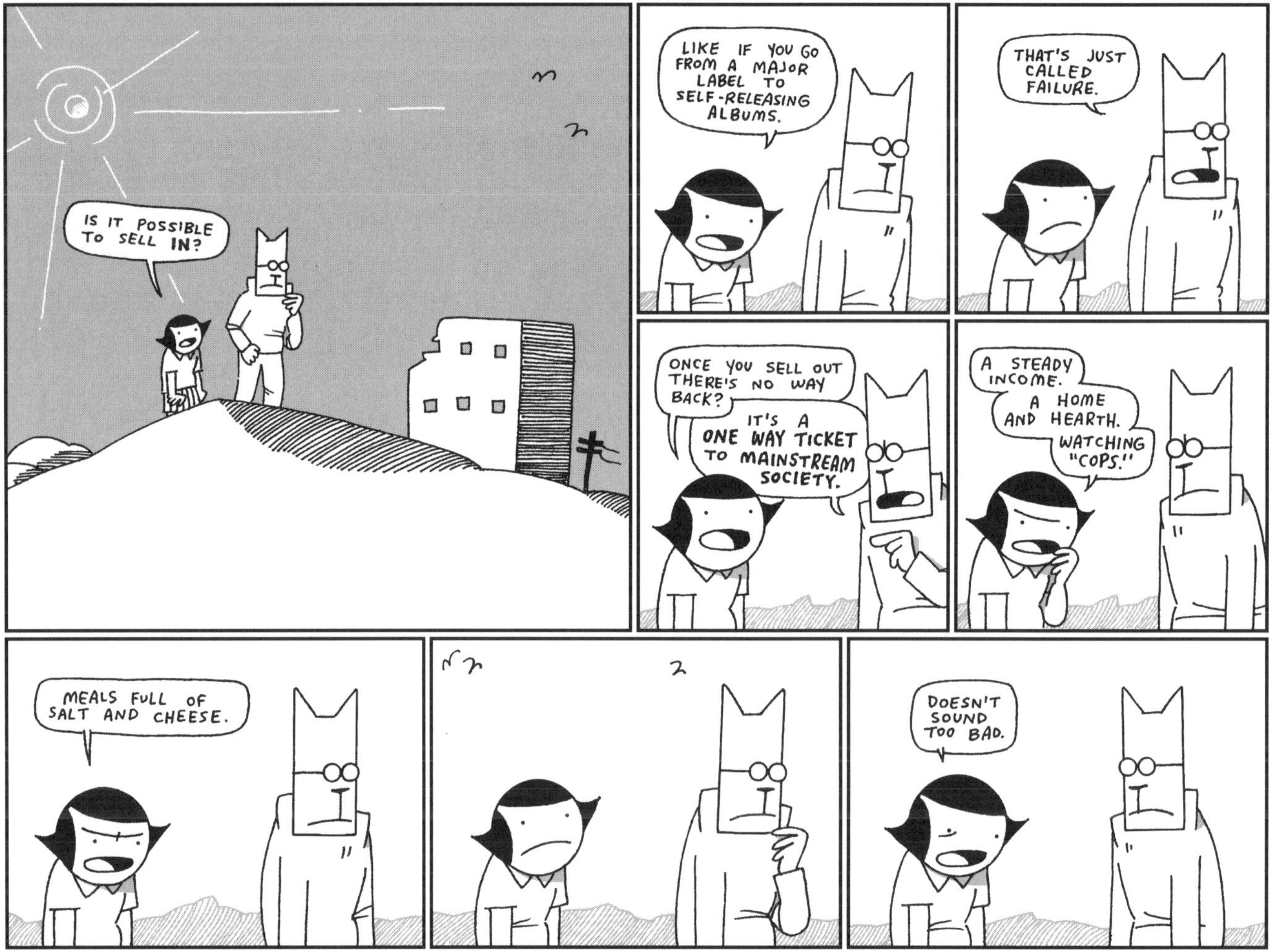
IS IT POSSIBLE TO SELL IN?
LIKE IF YOU GO FROM A MAJOR LABEL TO SELF-RELEASING ALBUMS.
THAT'S JUST CALLED FAILURE.
ONCE YOU SELL OUT THERE'S NO WAY BACK?
IT'S A ONE WAY TICKET TO MAINSTREAM SOCIETY.
A STEADY INCOME.
A HOME AND HEARTH.
WATCHING "COPS."
MEALS FULL OF SALT AND CHEESE.
DOESN'T SOUND TOO BAD.

ARE YOU GOING?
ARE YOU SELLING?
OUT?
NEVER!
TALK IS TALK
AND COMFORT IS COMFORT.
MARZIPAN DOESN'T STOP BEING MARZIPAN JUST BECAUSE YOU SHAPE IT LIKE LITTLE FRUITS.
I DON'T NEED MAINSTREAM SOCIETY NOT ONE LITTLE BIT!
CASH
DEATH
OBSCURITY
DEATH
BESIDES
THINK OF ALL THE TIME I SAVE
NOT PLANNING A DREAM WEDDING.

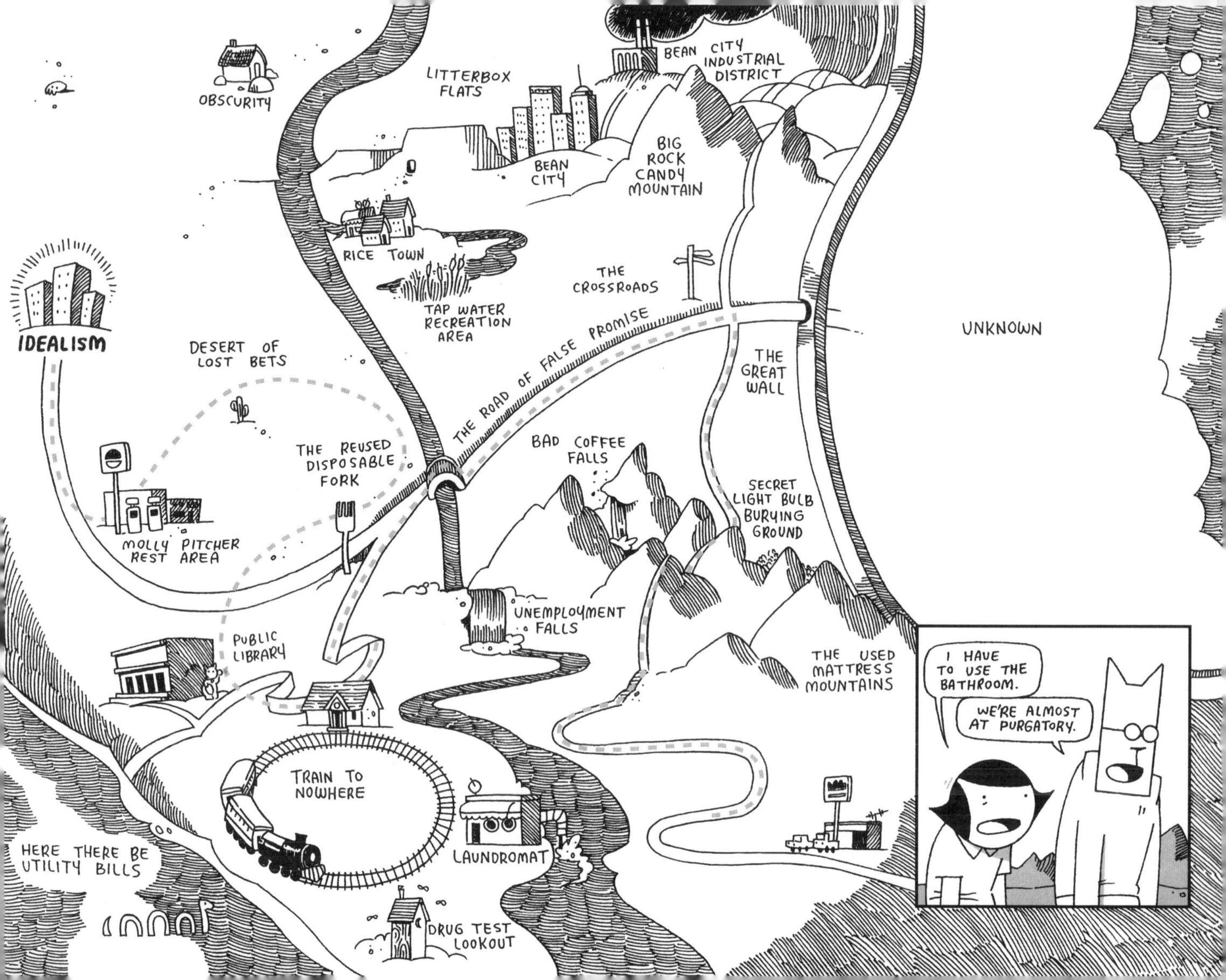
OBSCURITY
LITTERBOX FLATS
BEAN CITY INDUSTRIAL DISTRICT
BEAN CITY
BIG ROCK CANDY MOUNTAIN
RICE TOWN
TAP WATER RECREATION AREA
THE CROSSROADS
IDEALISM
DESERT OF LOST BETS
THE ROAD OF FALSE PROMISE
UNKNOWN
THE GREAT WALL
THE REUSED DISPOSABLE FORK
BAD COFFEE FALLS
SECRET LIGHT BULB BURYING GROUND
MOLLY PITCHER REST AREA
UNEMPLOYMENT FALLS
PUBLIC LIBRARY
THE USED MATTRESS MOUNTAINS
TRAIN TO NOWHERE
LAUNDROMAT
HERE THERE BE UTILITY BILLS
DRUG TEST LOOKOUT
I HAVE TO USE THE BATHROOM.
WE'RE ALMOST AT PURGATORY.

REG $ .00
PLUS $ .00
SUPR $. 0
POGS
POGS
POGS
POGS
VHS
2 DAY
RENT
RUBIN +ED
O'DOUL'S
OOH!
SUGAR FREE
CAN I GET CHANGE?
NO.

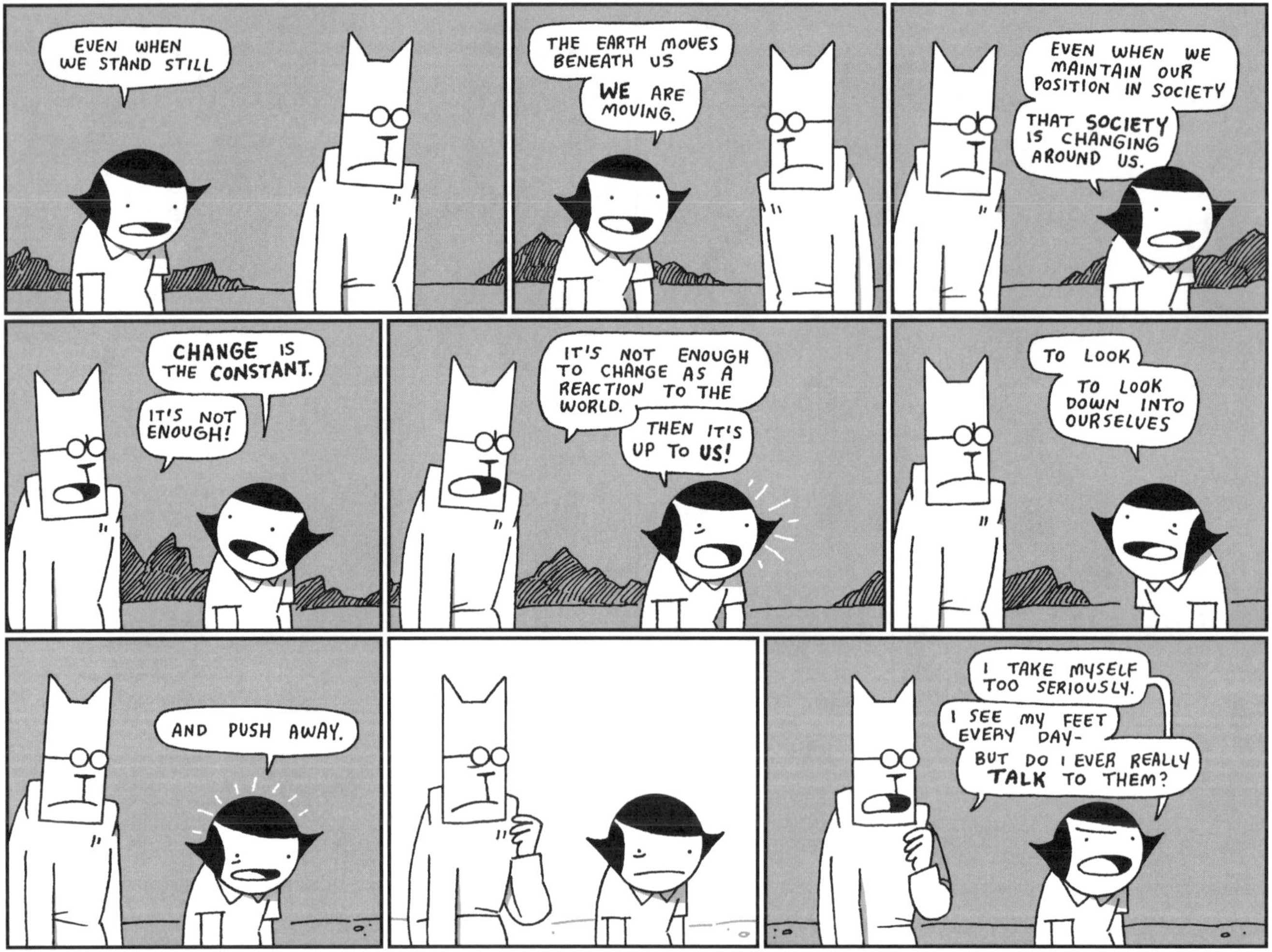
EVEN WHEN WE STAND STILL
THE EARTH MOVES BENEATH US
WE ARE MOVING.
EVEN WHEN WE MAINTAIN OUR POSITION IN SOCIETY
THAT SOCIETY IS CHANGING AROUND US.
CHANGE IS THE CONSTANT.
IT'S NOT ENOUGH!
IT'S NOT ENOUGH TO CHANGE AS A REACTION TO THE WORLD.
THEN IT'S UP TO US!
TO LOOK
TO LOOK DOWN INTO OURSELVES
AND PUSH AWAY.
I TAKE MYSELF TOO SERIOUSLY.
I SEE MY FEET EVERY DAY-
BUT DO I EVER REALLY TALK TO THEM?

Voter Resignation

ROCK THE VOTE
VOTE OR DIE
EVEN THAT VESTIGIAL SLOGAN SPEAKS TO A TIME OF FALSE HOPES
A TIME NOW GONE.
AMERICA HAS SPENT THE LAST EIGHT YEARS DIGGING ITSELF INTO A HOLE
ADDING PLUMBING
AND SMACKING A PORCELAIN ARMCHAIR ON TOP.
LET'S GET AMERICA OUT OF THE TOILET!
AMERICA OUT OF THE TOILET IN 2008.

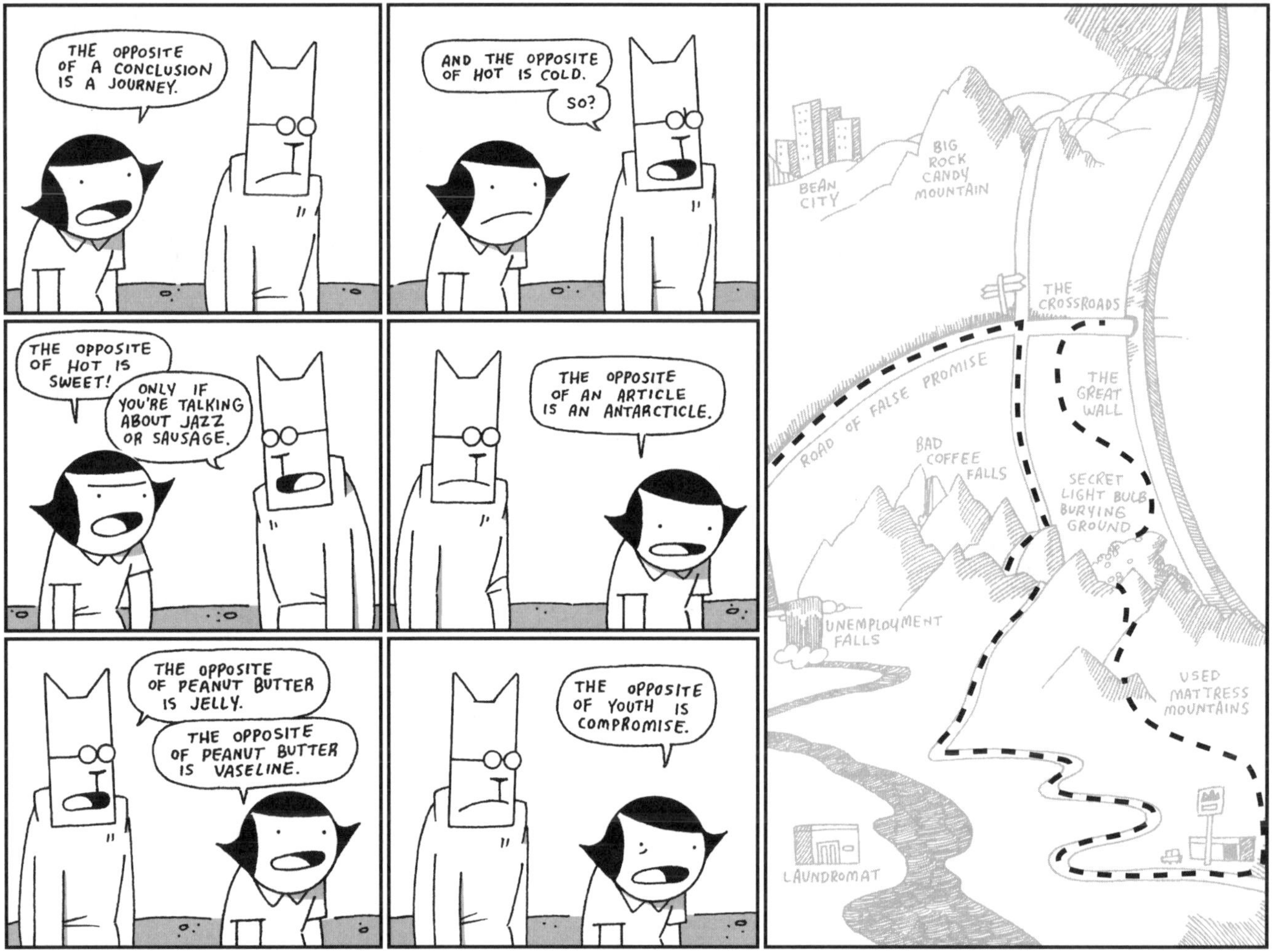
THE OPPOSITE OF A CONCLUSION IS A JOURNEY.
AND THE OPPOSITE OF HOT IS COLD.
SO?
THE OPPOSITE OF HOT IS SWEET!
ONLY IF YOU'RE TALKING ABOUT JAZZ OR SAUSAGE.
THE OPPOSITE OF AN ARTICLE IS AN ANTARCTICLE.
THE OPPOSITE OF PEANUT BUTTER IS JELLY.
THE OPPOSITE OF PEANUT BUTTER IS VASELINE.
THE OPPOSITE OF YOUTH IS COMPROMISE.
BEAN CITY
BIG ROCK CANDY MOUNTAIN
THE CROSSROADS
ROAD OF FALSE PROMISE
THE GREAT WALL
BAD COFFEE FALLS
SECRET LIGHT BULB BURYING GROUND
UNEMPLOYMENT FALLS
USED MATTRESS MOUNTAINS
LAUNDROMAT

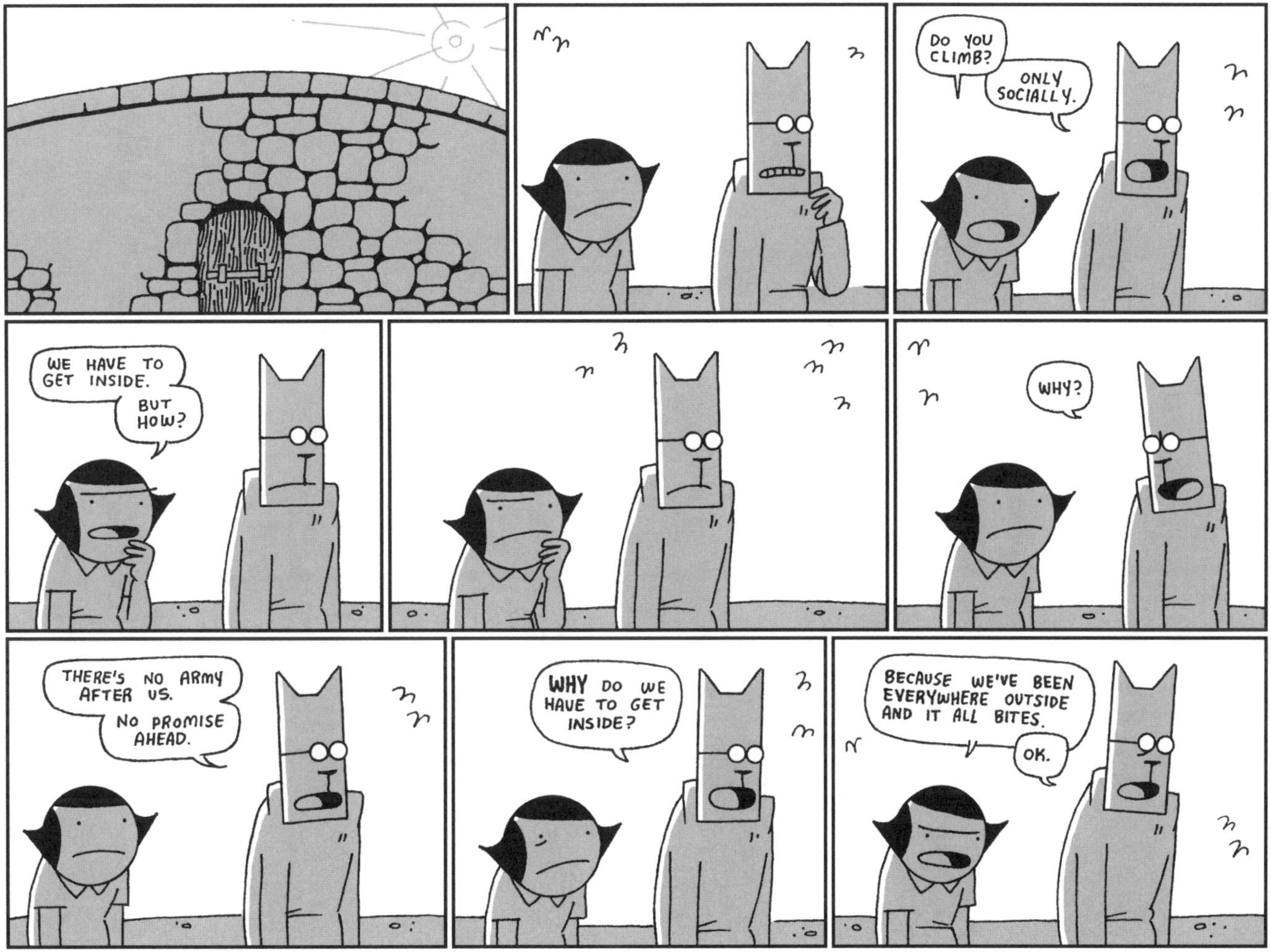

DO YOU CLIMB?
ONLY SOCIALLY.
WE HAVE TO GET INSIDE.
BUT HOW?
WHY?
THERE'S NO ARMY AFTER US.
NO PROMISE AHEAD.
WHY DO WE HAVE TO GET INSIDE?
BECAUSE WE'VE BEEN EVERYWHERE OUTSIDE AND IT ALL BITES.
OK.

SHHHHP
CAN I TAKE YOUR ORDER?
WE'RE STILL DECIDING.
WHERE IS THIS?
MECCA, GUYS.
COMPROMISE.
YOU AREN'T PILGRIMS?
DO WE LOOK LIKE WE'RE PROGRESSING?
I DON'T REMEMBER HEADING TO COMPROMISE.
EVERYONE SHOWS UP EVENTUALLY.
JUST GIVE OVER YOUR PASSPORTS AAAAND-
STAMP STAMP STAMP
AND YOU'RE CLEAR TO GO!

IF WE ENTER CAN WE LEAVE?
WHY WOULD YOU WANT TO LEAVE?
WE HAVE FLAT SCREEN TVS.
DO YOU LIKE WHAT YOU DO?
IT'S A JOB.

Easy As

A, B, C.
A, B, C.
A
B
C
ABC
A.
B.
C.
WHAT'S YOUR FAVORITE KIND OF HEPATITIS?
CHOCOLATE.

Trinity

WE HAVE TWO SHADOW COMPANIONS THROUGHOUT LIFE.
GEORGE AND BESS?
SIMON AND GARFUNKEL?
NEED AND WANT.
TO NEED IS TO LIVE.
TO WANT IS TO LIVE IN SOCIETY.
BUT WHAT IF WE COULD BREAK FREE FROM WANT
WHAT COULD THAT MEAN?
WHAT IF WE DIDN'T WANT ANYTHING?
YOU'D GET A LOT OF SOCKS FOR CHRISTMAS.

OH
NUTS

FISSSH

BZZZT
WHAT'S THE POINT?
I SIT AROUND WITH THESE
FEELINGS.
OTHER PEOPLE SIT AROUND WITH CABLE.
AT LEAST THAT'S INTERESTING.
FEELINGS WITHOUT ACTION ARE WORTH A FIST FULL OF SNOT!
ACTION WITHOUT FEELING IS THE COLD DOMAIN OF OFFICE DRONES AND PSYCHOPATHS.
SO ACTION AND FEELING FEED ON EACH OTHER.
TOGETHER MEANING EVERYTHING.
APART MEANING NOTHING.
LAUREL AND HARDY.
TONY ORLANDO AND DOOM.

The Alone Ranger

FIRST THEY CAME FOR THE PLATES
AND I DIDN'T SPEAK UP
BECAUSE I WASN'T A PLATE

Plate Byronics

DO YOU EVER WANT TO BE AN ARTIST?
WHAT'S THE POINT?
EVERYTHING'S ALREADY BEEN MADE.
THE ARTIST IS THE EXPIRED IDEAL OF A DEAD AGE.
SOME ROMANTIC FIGURE STANDING OUTSIDE OF SOCIETY SPEAKING TRUTH TO POWER.
WELL WELCOME TO THE MODERN WORLD!
THAT HOMOGENOUS SOCIETY IS GONE -
SOCIETY HAS FRACTURED -
AND IN THE MILLIONS OF SHARDS IS ROOM FOR EVERYONE -
WHETHER THEY LIKE IT OR NOT.
THERE IS NO POWER.
THERE IS NO TRUTH.
WE'RE CONSUMERS IN NICHE MARKETS ASSEMBLING A SELF THROUGH CHOICE.
THE ARTIST IS DEAD!
THE FUTURE IS CURATORIAL!
DO YOU EVER WANT TO BE AN ARTIST?
WHAT'S THE POINT? I'M IMMORTAL ALREADY.

YOUTH IS WASTED ON THE STUPID.

Bad News Bear

BANG BANG BANG BANG BANG
WE'RE GOING TO A MOVIE!
GET YOUR COAT!
WHAT MOVIE?
IT'S ABOUT-
IT'S ABOUT A GROUP OF PLUCKY MISFITS-
LOSERS.
OUTSIDERS!
AND-
AND THEY TAKE ON THIS BIG RICH DISCIPLINED CORPORATE TEAM-
AND NO ONE THINKS THEY CAN PULL IT OFF-
EVERYONE TOTALLY EXPECTS THEM TO BE CRUSHED, BUT-
I'M NOT GOING TO ANOTHER DOCUMENTARY ABOUT THE WAR IN IRAQ.

Curses

IT WAS A YEAR AGO TODAY-
I WAS ASKED FOR DIRECTIONS TO WASHINGTON SQUARE PARK BY AN OLD GYPSY LADY IN AN I ♥ NY TEE SHIRT AND FANNY PACK.
WHEN I CORRECTED HER PRONUNCIATION OF HOUSTON-
THE WORLD STOPPED FOR A SECOND.
BIRDS EVERYWHERE TOOK TO THE SKY.
EVER SINCE THEN I'VE BEEN CURSED.
STUDENT LOANS?
WORSE!
CREDIT CARD DEBT.
STREET LIGHTS GO OUT AS I WALK BY.
LOAVES OF BREAD TURN TO MOLD AT MY TOUCH.
ANYTHING I DO
ANYWHERE I GO
ANY PLAN I MAKE-
ONE WEEK LATER
THERE'S AN ARTICLE ABOUT IT IN THE NEW YORK TIMES STYLE SECTION.

Priorities

THE ARTIST
DOES NOT CHOOSE MONEY.
THE ARTIST STANDS ALONE AGAINST THE ONSLAUGHT OF CAREERS AND CREATIVE PROFESSIONALS AND SELF-DEFINITION BY CONSPICUOUS CONSUMPTION-
THE IPODS AND CELL PHONES AND DVD COLLECTIONS AND HIGH DEFINITION TELEVISIONS AND WIIS AND PEDIGREED DOGS AND MEALS AT RESTAURANTS ASSUMED TO BE THE BARE MINIMUM OF SUCCESSFUL EXISTENCE-
THE ARTIST DOES NOT CHOOSE MONEY.
THE ARTIST CHOOSES EGO.

H&R BLOCK
OPEN

Sophie's

HOW DO YOU DECIDE?
IT'S HARD ENOUGH PICKING OUT A SHIRT IN THE MORNING-
A PARKING SPACE-
TEA OR COFFEE-
THIS CONSTANT LOW-LEVEL PRESSURE
KNOWING THAT AT ANY MOMENT YOU WILL BE GIVEN THE OPPORTUNITY TO BE WRONG
AGAIN AND AGAIN AND AGAIN.
I WANT IT TO BE EASY.
I WANT MY CHOICES MADE BY A BENEVOLENT GOD
OR A CIVIC LEADER
OR A MUSICIAN I PARTICULARLY ADMIRE.
I WOULD TAKE THAT.
I WANT SOMEONE ELSE TO SPIN THE WHEEL OF FATE.
I WANT TO LET DESTINY TAKE ITS COURSE.
JUST DECIDE ON A DAMN SANDWICH ALREADY.
SHUT UP REUBEN.
YOU TOO SLOPPY JOE.
OK.

A Variety of Stories On That Theme

STORIES YOU WILL NEVER HEAR ON THIS AMERICAN LIFE.
A MAN LOOKS INTO HIS FAMILY'S PAST-
AND IS BORED BY WHAT HE FINDS.
A WOMAN INVESTIGATES AN ODD OCCURENCE THAT HAPPENED ACROSS THE STREET FROM HER CHILDHOOD HOME-
BUT THE ANSWERS SHE GETS
ARE THE ONES SHE EXPECTED.
TWO CHILDREN THINK THEIR PARENTS MIGHT BE HIDING A SECRET
AND DECIDE TO INVESTIGATE
AND THEY DO NOT REGRET IT.

Mutualism

HOW MUCH OF OUR INTEREST IN MOVIES AND MUSIC IS THEIR CONTENT
AND HOW MUCH IS OUR NEEDS?
DO I COLLECT RECORDS BECAUSE I'M REALLY INTO MINIMAL SYNTH POP
OR BECAUSE I'M REALLY INTO MINUTIAE?
DO I ENJOY HISTORICAL BIOGRAPHIES OR DO I ENJOY THINKING OF MYSELF AS THE SORT OF PERSON WHO ENJOYS HISTORICAL BIOGRAPHIES?
ARE WE CAPABLE OF SUBTEXT-FREE ENJOYMENT AT ALL?
YOU'RE BUYING INTO THE MYTH OF THE SUBCONSCIOUS MIND!
ARE OUR IDEAS OF PLEASURE SHAPED BY OUR NATIONALITY-
UPBRINGING- GENDER- EDUCATION-
JOB-
PLACE IN SOCIETY-
CIRCLE OF FRIENDS-
SURE!
IF YOU ENJOY SOMETHING, YOU ENJOY IT.
SO ENJOY IT!
HMPH.
MYTH OF THE SUBCONSCIOUS
MY BOOT!

Hot and Cool

WHAT ARE YOU UP TO TONIGHT?
I-
I WHAT?
IF I SAY WATCHING TELEVISION YOU'RE JUST GOING TO START SHOUTING.
WATCHING TELEVISION!?!
COULD ANY MEDIUM BE MORE PASSIVE?
PEOPLE WATCH MOVIES.
AT LEAST PICKING A MOVIE INVOLVES SOME DEGREE OF DELIBERATION!
TELEVISION IS AN ENDLESS MULTI-HEADED SPEW OF AUDIO AND VIDEO
AT LEAST MOVIES END.
MAYBE WATCHING TELEVISION WAS PASSIVE WHEN THERE WERE THREE NETWORKS AND YOU HAD TO GET UP TO CHANGE THE CHANNEL-
BUT THAT'S NOT HOW PEOPLE WATCH TELEVISION ANY MORE!
SURE TELEVISION'S A HYDRA OF NEVERENDING SUB-PAR IMAGES AND SOUND.
BUT PEOPLE TIVO- THEY FAST FORWARD AND REWIND-
THEY CHANGE CHANNELS CONSTANTLY-
YOU SAID THE FUTURE WAS CURATORIAL-
WELL THIS IS PEOPLE ACTIVELY CURATING!
BECAUSE THEY MADE MICROWAVE POPCORN DURING A COMMERCIAL BREAK IN TWO AND A HALF MEN?
OH
LIKE THE GUGGENHEIM HASN'T HAD SOME CLUNKERS TOO.

Processor

WHAT IS IT THAT WE DO IN OUR DAILY LIVES?
SUFFER?
WE TAKE THE RAW MATERIAL OF THE WORLD AROUND US
AND PROCESS IT INTO THE FINISHED MATERIAL OF OUR THOUGHTS, OUR CONVERSATION, OUR ART.
WHAT DO WE DO WHEN WE WATCH TELEVISION?
WE CHOOSE TO VIEW A STREAM OF MATERIAL THAT HAS BEEN FINISHED FOR US.
I EAT NACHOS.
NOW
WHAT IF WE COULD CONVERT THIS PROCESSED STREAM BACK TO RAW MATERIAL?
TZZzzp
LIKE MOST TELEVISIONS THIS ALLOWS YOU TO ADJUST THE BRIGHTNESS AND SATURATION
PLUS IT HAS SEPARATE CONTROLS FOR THE AUDIO AND VIDEO
AND THERE'S NO CHANNEL DISPLAY
MAKING MATCHING THE AUDIO AND VIDEO DIFFICULT AND TIME-CONSUMING!
QUESTION.
I THINK YOU'RE MISSING THE POINT OF TELEVISION.
I AM TRYING TO SAVE THE WORLD!

Habitrail Heart

I WANT TO ENCOURAGE DELIBERATE ACTION-
THE VIEWER TAKING AN AGGRESSIVE ROLE IN WHAT IS BEING VIEWED.
CONVERTING A PASSIVE MEDIUM TO AN ACTIVE ONE!
THE INTERNET IS AN ACTIVE MEDIUM!
BUT-
WE WAKE UP
WE CHECK OUR EMAIL.
WE EAT A SANDWICH
WE READ ASK METAFILTER.
WE HABITUATE TO ANYTHING.
ONLY THE UNKNOWN FORCES US INTO DELIBERATE ACTION.
LIKE WHEN YOU'RE FALLING
AND TIME STOPS
AND YOU SEE YOUR EVERY OPTION LINED UP BEFORE YOU
AND YOU DELIBERATE
AND YOU CHOOSE
AS YOU HEAD TOWARDS THE GROUND.

OOF

AND STAY OUT!
SLAM
YOU COULDN'T TALK POLITELY ABOUT WHOLE FOODS FOR HALF AN HOUR?
WELL
WE'LL NEVER HAVE TO LISTEN TO JENS LEKMAN AGAIN.
YOU'LL BE BACK!

I'M NEVER GOING BACK.
BUT WE COULD-
OF COURSE WE COULD-
THEY NEED US!
ANYONE LIVING OUTSIDE OF COMPROMISE DELEGITIMIZES EVERYONE INSIDE!
CITIZENS OF COMPROMISE DON'T WANT TO BELIEVE THERE'S A WORLD OUTSIDE
THAT WOULD MEAN THEY MADE A CHOICE TO LIVE THERE!
WELL I CHOOSE TO LIVE OUTSIDE!
AND I'M NEVER GOING BACK.
I'M TELLING EVERYONE YOU HAD AN IPHONE.
DON'T YOU DARE!

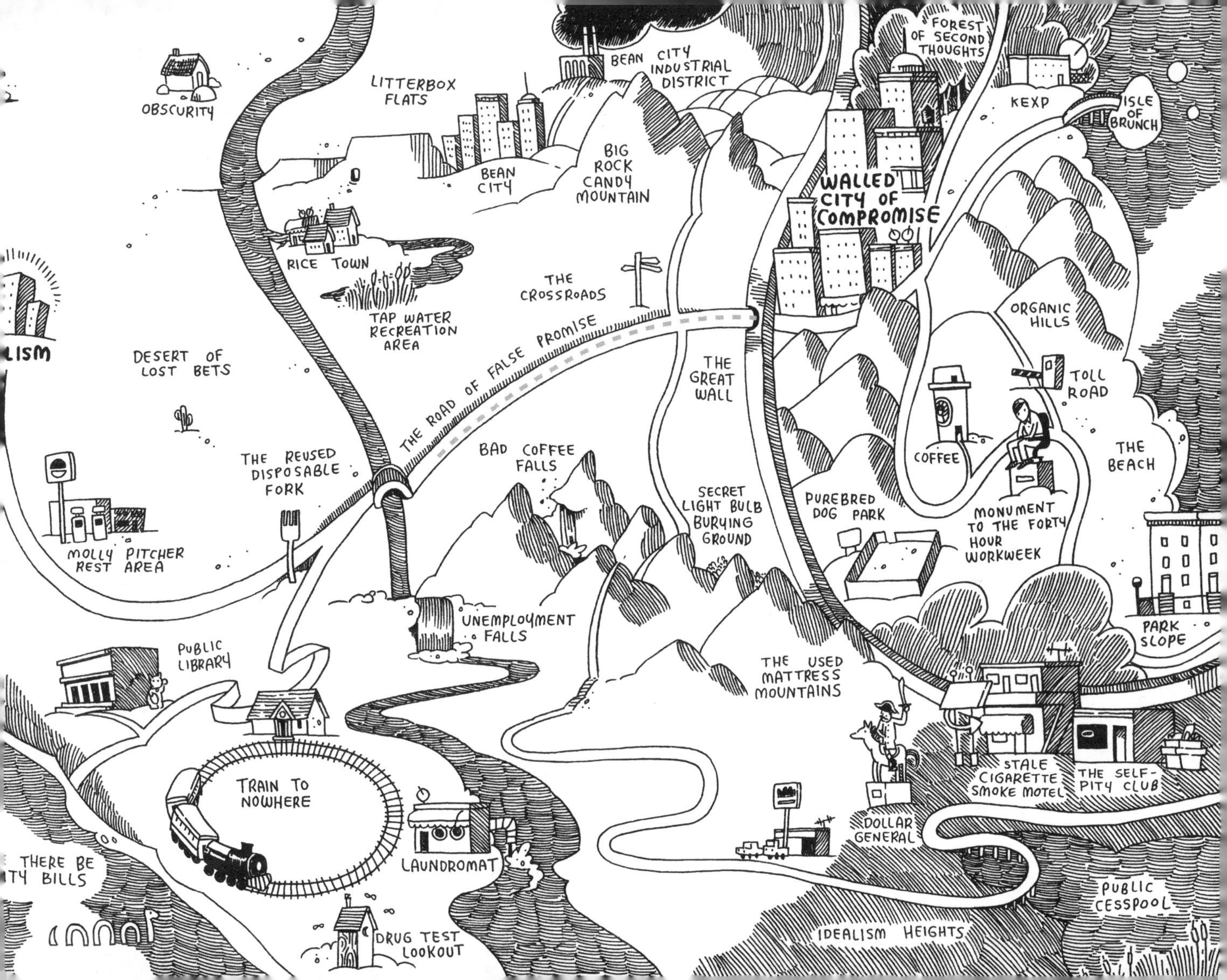

OBSCURITY
LITTERBOX FLATS
BEAN CITY INDUSTRIAL DISTRICT
FOREST OF SECOND THOUGHTS
KEXP
ISLE OF BRUNCH
BEAN CITY
BIG ROCK CANDY MOUNTAIN
WALLED CITY OF COMPROMISE
RICE TOWN
TAP WATER RECREATION AREA
THE CROSSROADS
LISM
DESERT OF LOST BETS
THE ROAD OF FALSE PROMISE
THE GREAT WALL
ORGANIC HILLS
TOLL ROAD
COFFEE
THE BEACH
THE REUSED DISPOSABLE FORK
BAD COFFEE FALLS
SECRET LIGHT BULB BURYING GROUND
PUREBRED DOG PARK
MONUMENT TO THE FORTY HOUR WORKWEEK
MOLLY PITCHER REST AREA
UNEMPLOYMENT FALLS
PARK SLOPE
PUBLIC LIBRARY
THE USED MATTRESS MOUNTAINS
STALE CIGARETTE SMOKE MOTEL
THE SELF-PITY CLUB
TRAIN TO NOWHERE
DOLLAR GENERAL
THERE BE
TY BILLS
LAUNDROMAT
PUBLIC CESSPOOL
DRUG TEST LOOKOUT
IDEALISM HEIGHTS

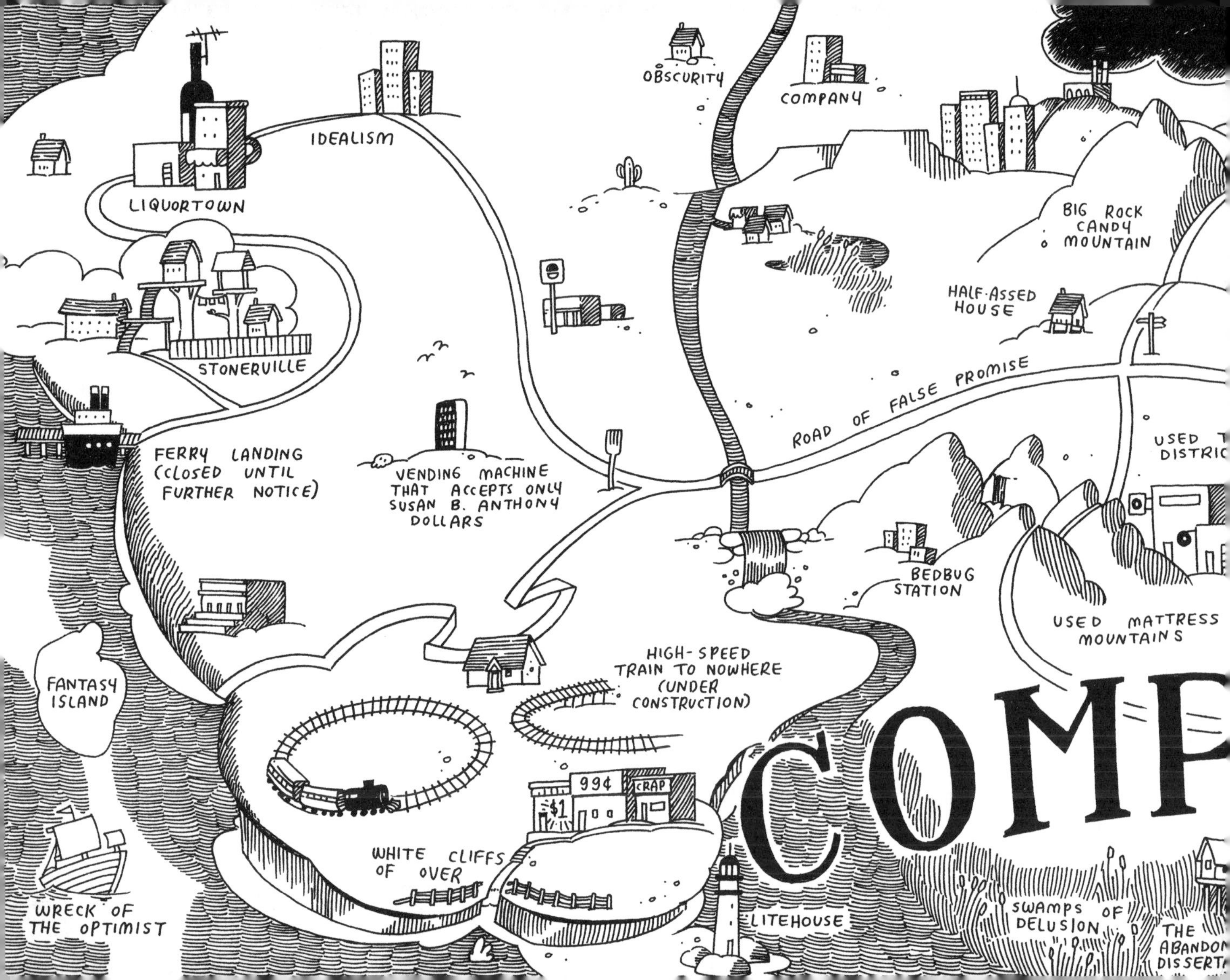

OBSCURITY
COMPANY
IDEALISM
LIQUORTOWN
BIG ROCK CANDY MOUNTAIN
HALF-ASSED HOUSE
STONERVILLE
ROAD OF FALSE PROMISE
FERRY LANDING (CLOSED UNTIL FURTHER NOTICE)
VENDING MACHINE THAT ACCEPTS ONLY SUSAN B. ANTHONY DOLLARS
USED T
DISTRIC
BEDBUG STATION
USED MATTRESS MOUNTAINS
FANTASY ISLAND
HIGH-SPEED TRAIN TO NOWHERE (UNDER CONSTRUCTION)
COMP
99¢
CRAP
$1
WHITE CLIFFS OF OVER
WRECK OF THE OPTIMIST
LITEHOUSE
SWAMPS OF DELUSION
THE ABANDON
DISSERT

FOREST OF SECOND THOUGHTS
THE MORTGAGE
THE GREAT HALL OF PEOPLE YOU USED TO KNOW
WALLED CITY OF COMPROMISE
TIDAL FORCES OF CONVENIENCE
THAT OBTUSE MOTIVE
THE RAMEKIN
MOUNT SEDENTARY
MOCACHINO TAR PITS
THE SOFT EMBRACE OF SLEEP
MINI GOLF
ROMISE
LITTLE MORALITY
PUBLIC CESSPOOL
COMPROMISE STATE UNIVERSITY
IDEALISM HEIGHTS
BIKE PATH
STORE BRAND SPRINGS

TOFU
I CAN'T KEEP UP WITH MY RSS FEEDS.

CLICK
CLICK
CLICK
CLICK
CLICK
IT'S EASY TO ROMANTICIZE THE PAST.
BUT STILL
I ENVY LIFE IN A TIME OF JUST THREE CHANNELS.
WATCHING TWELVE DOGS BALANCE PLATES ON THEIR NOSES ISN'T ANY MORE ENTERTAINING THAN "ACE OF CAKES."
NOT BECAUSE OF THE CONTENT-
BUT THE IDEA OF MEDIA THAT UNIFIES A CULTURE INSTEAD OF DIVIDING IT.
MONOCULTURE
WELL YEAH
CULTURE THAT SPEAKS WITH ONE LANGUAGE-
AND A POPULACE THAT CAN UNDERSTAND ONE ANOTHER!
EVERYONE LISTENED TO THE BEATLES.
AND IT'S A LOT EASIER TO UNIFY A CULTURE WHEN THE ONLY VALID VOICES ARE WHITE, MALE AND WESTERN!
MONOCULTURE ISN'T JUST EVERYONE WATCHING THE ED SULLIVAN SHOW - IT'S BUYING ALL YOUR CLOTHES AT SEARS.
EATING MICROWAVED SALISBURY STEAK FOR DINNER EVERY TUESDAY AND THURSDAY-
THE SPIRITUAL POVERTY OF LIFE BEFORE GLOBALISM!
THE BEATLES USED A SITAR.
THAT'S GIVING RANCH DRESSING CREDIT FOR DISCOVERING PAD THAI.

GLOBALISM GIVES US NEW BETTER DIFFERENT OPTIONS-
SO THE WHOLE WORLD CAN LOOK LIKE AMERICA?
SO AMERICA LOOKS LIKE THE WORLD!
CITIES MAYBE
BUT ONCE YOU HEAD INTO THE WORLD'S COUNTRYSIDE IT'S LIKE GOING BACK IN
YES!
WHAT SEEMS MORE DISTANT-
FIVE YEARS AGO OR JAPAN?
THAT'S APPLES AND-
-AND HAND GRENADES.
THE SEDENTARY FAMILY-
LIVING AS THEY'VE LIVED FOR GENERATIONS-
ON THEIR ANCESTOR'S LAND, AMONG THEIR ANCESTOR'S BELONGINGS,
NEVER TRAVELING FURTHER THAN THE NEAREST TOWN-
IF THE WORLD WAS UNKNOWN
THE PAST WAS CLOSE TO THEM.
BUT NOW
BECAUSE CULTURE CHANGES SO FAST BECAUSE THERE IS SO MUCH OF IT FROM ALL OVER
BECAUSE OF THE SPEED OF AIR TRAVEL, THE EASE OF GLOBAL COMMUNICATION-
THE FOREIGNNESS OF PLACE IS SUPPLANTED
BY THE FOREIGNNESS OF TIME.

WE'RE BACK!
YOU LEFT?

A Cultural History of I Don't Own a Television

I DON'T OWN A TE-LE-VISION.
I DON'T OWN A TELEVISION.
I DON'T OWN A TELEVISION.
I DON'T OWN A TELEVISION!
I DON'T OWN A TELEVISION.
HOWL
I DON'T OWN A TELEVISION.
NPR
I DON'T OWN A TELEVISION.
I DON'T OWN A TELEVISION.
I OWN A HOME ENTERTAINMENT SYSTEM.

This Means War

...NPR BUSINESS NEWS STARTS WITH JUNKING YOUR ELECTRONIC...
...THE EPA'S LATEST FIGURES SHOW THAT AMERICANS THREW...
CLICK
BADADA WA WOOWAWAWA BIP BOO BOP BOP BOP BEE BEE BOO
CLICK
CLICK
CLICK
CLICK
CLICK
CLICK
...AND THE LAST WORD IN BUSINESS TODAY IS...
MORAL SUPERIORITY IN ANY CONFLICT IS DETERMINED **NOT** BY **WHY** YOU FIGHT BUT **HOW.**
CLICK
CLICK
SNAP
...PLAYING GAMES WITH THE FACES...
...YOU SAID THE MAN IN THE GABARDINE SUIT WAS A SPY...

Nature's Doomed Adolescents

I CAN'T WAIT FOR HIGH SCHOOL!
THAT DOOMED TRANSITIONAL STAGE-
YOU WHAT?
HIGH SCHOOL IS OUR LAST CHANCE!
TO SELL BEACH TOWELS FOR THE MARCHING BAND?
TO DEAL WITH ALL ELEMENTS OF SOCIETY AS EQUALS.
BEFORE BEING BRANDED AND SHUFFLED OFF TO THE WORK AND EDUCATION SOCIETY HAS DEEMED APPROPRIATE FOR US.
MAYBE THE DOOM IS WHAT'S ENTICING.
ONE BRIEF MOMENT OF STRANGE INCONSEQUENTIAL IRRATIONAL BELIEF.
BEFORE CAREERS AND KIDS AND COMPROMISE
AND THE METEORITE HITS
AND THE CEILING FALLS IN.
OR WE COULD BE DINOSAURS.
DO THEY HAVE A NEWSPAPER?

Proverbs and Plagues

WHEN LIFE GIVES YOU LEMONS MAKE LEMONADE.
WHEN LIFE GIVES YOU LIMES?
GIN AND TONIC!
WHEN LIFE HANDS YOU A PICKLE
ASK TO SUBSTITUTE COLESLAW.
WHEN LIFE GIVES MARGARINE
PRAY FOR BUTTER.
WHEN LIFE GIVES YOU ASTRONAUTS
INSIST ON THE FUTILITY OF THE SHUTTLE PROGRAM.
WHEN LIFE GIVES YOU SHORT SHORTS-
ASK WHERE THEY'RE FROM.
WHEN LIFE GIVES YOU A CAR
LAUGH AT PEOPLE ON THE BUS.
WHEN LIFE GIVES YOU PUDDING
KEEP WALKING.

Reincarnation

LPS TO CDS TO MP3S- MUSIC CONTINUES TO DECORPOREALIZE.
BUT WHEN I LOOK AT LISTS OF MP3S I FEEL THE SAME SENSE OF OWNERSHIP THAT I DO WHEN BROWSING MY BOOK CASE.
SCARCITY.
WHAT?
WHAT IF YOU DELETE AN MP3 AND YOU CAN NEVER FIND IT AGAIN?
WITHOUT SCARCITY OWNERSHIP MAKES NO SENSE.
SCARCITY.
A LAGGING LEGACY OF MUSIC'S TIME AS A PHYSICAL OBJECT.
ONCE UPON A TIME MUSIC WAS SOMETHING YOU MADE OR SAW MADE, SOMETHING THAT LIVED IN A MOMENT AND WAS **GONE**.
AND THEN PEOPLE BEGAN RECORDING MUSIC-SHADOWS OF REAL, LIVE PERFORMANCES FOR THOSE NOT FORTUNATE ENOUGH TO WITNESS THEM.
BUT WHEN WE CHOOSE **WHICH** MOMENT TO RECORD
WE **PRIORITIZE** IT-
WHEN WE CHOOSE WHICH MOMENT TO **RELEASE** AS A **PHYSICAL OBJECT**
WE PRIORITIZE **THAT.**
AND THE **RECORDING** BECOMES REALITY, AND THE MOMENTS OF PERFORMANCE OR RECITATION OR BARROOM SINGALONG ARE **ITS** SHADOWS.
BUT NOW **EVERYTHING** IS RECORDED-
AND THE **OBJECT** IS UNNECESSARY.
AND THAT PRIORITY IS GONE.
AND THAT PRIORITY IS GONE.
AND SO WE SAY GOODBYE TO 1957, WHEN RECORDS FIRST OUTSOLD SHEET MUSIC - TO THE DAY BEFORE YESTERDAY, WHEN EVERYONE'S EX-ROOMMATE SOLD ALL HER CDS ON EBAY - OUR ROGUE HALF-CENTURY OF **MUSIC** AS AN **OBJECT**.
SCARCITY
SCARCITY
SCARCITY

Exponential Bloat

WE DOWNLOAD MUSIC TO OWN IT.
WE DOWNLOAD MUSIC BECAUSE IT'S EASY!
POINTING-
CLICKING-
WAITING-
UPLOADING...
WAITING...
PODCASTS!
DOWNLOADING IS INCONVENIENT.
AND VERY FEW THINGS IN LIFE ARE STRONG ENOUGH TO WITHSTAND THE TIDAL FORCES OF CONVENIENCE.
IT'S NOT EXACTLY CRANKING UP THE PHONOGRAPH FOR TWO MINUTES OF MUSIC.
IT'S NOT CROSSING THE ROOM TO FLIP THE RECORD OVER FOR TWENTY MINUTES OF MUSIC.
IT'S NOT SEARCHING FOR THE REMOTE FOR THE FIVE CD CAROUSEL FOR 200 MINUTES OF MUSIC.
IT'S POINTING · CLICKING · WAITING-
FOR 200 HOURS OF MUSIC!
MORE!
THE NEXT STEP ISN'T MORE DOWNLOADING-
MORE OWNERSHIP-
IT ISN'T 2000 HOURS OR 20,000-
IT'S STREAMING. IT'S INFINITE!
SO IPODS ARE AN OLD TECHNOLOGY.
THAT EXPLAINS WHY I HAVE ONE.

SCARCITY
SCARCITY
SCARCITY

Matters of Taste

DING
RADIO!
RADIO IS CONVENIENT AND INFINITE.
THE RADIO PLAYS CRAP.
BUT-
AND IT'S NOT MY CRAP!

Natural Law

IT'S THE ADVANTAGE OF BROADCAST MEDIUM THAT YOU DON'T CONTROL WHAT YOU GET
SO INSTEAD
OF CHOOSING OUR OWN SOUNDTRACK, ONE IS IMPOSED
IS THAT THE TIME?
I SHOULD GET GOING.
IT'S JUST A
IT'S A WEEKLY THING.
THE OLD TECHNOLOGY SWAPMEET.
JUST A GROUP OF PEOPLE, SO...
IT'S MOSTLY ORGANIZATIONAL.
I SHOULD HEAD.
WHY WASN'T I INVITED?
YOU WERE GONE FOR FOUR MONTHS!
VERY FEW THINGS IN LIFE ARE STRONG ENOUGH TO WITHSTAND THE TIDAL FORCES OF CONVENIENCE.

A Pirate's Life

SOME PEOPLE ARE IN IT FOR THE ADVENTURE.
SOME LIKE THE CHALLENGE OF LIFE ON THE SEA.
SOME PEOPLE ARE IN IT FOR THE MONEY.
SOME PEOPLE ARE ALWAYS IN IT FOR THE MONEY.
AND SOME PEOPLE JOIN FOR THE FREEDOM.
THAT RARE LIFE SPENT OUTSIDE SOCIETY'S NARROW BOUNDS.
THE COMRADERY OF THE FALLEN.
SINGING, LOOTING, HOLLERING.
MAKING YOUR OWN HOURS.
WORKING FROM HOME.
SOME PEOPLE JUST WANT TO MEET PARROTS.

The Ruler

A FOOT?
I SAY IT'S A STICK.

Model UN

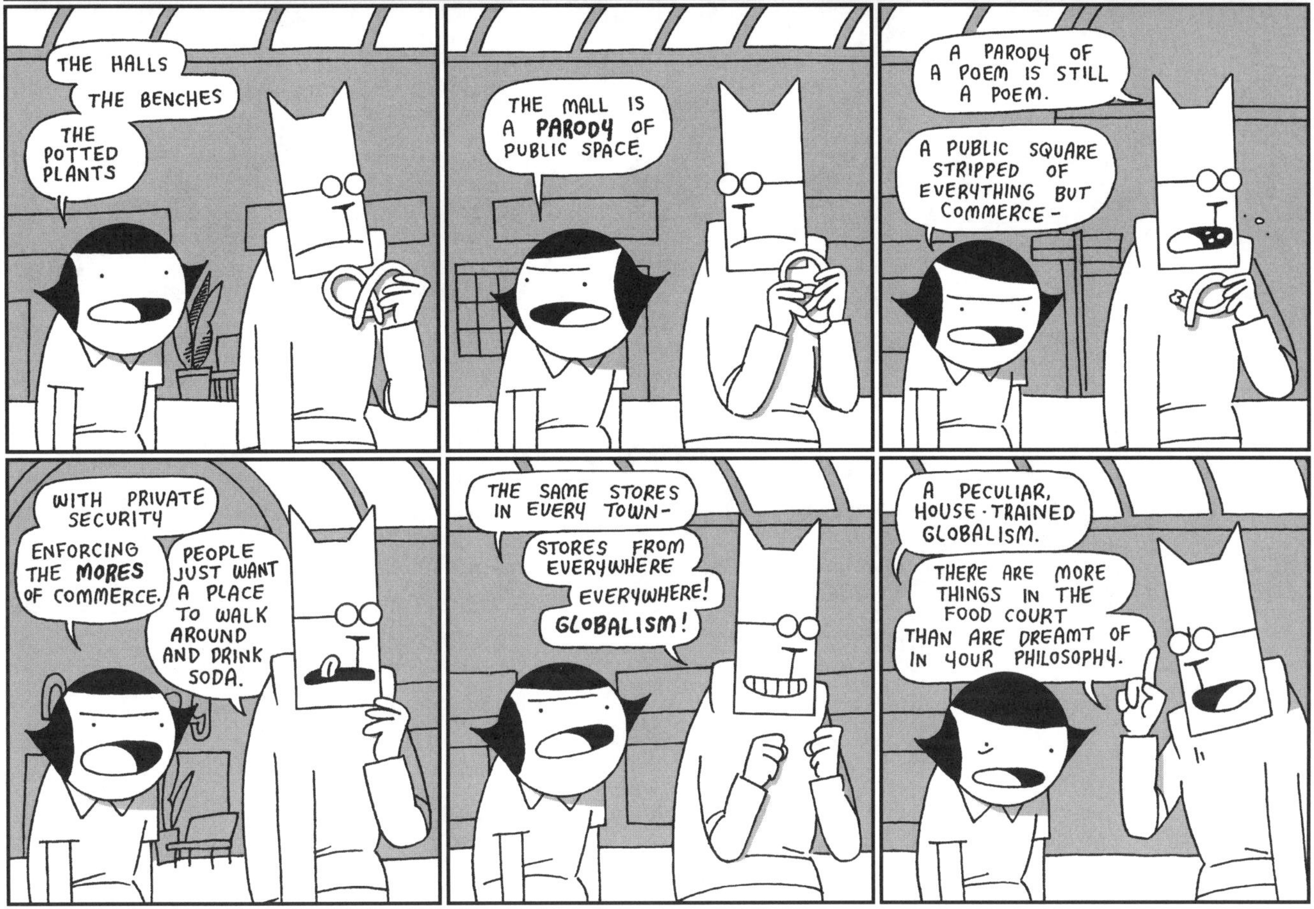
THE HALLS
THE BENCHES
THE POTTED PLANTS
THE MALL IS A **PARODY** OF PUBLIC SPACE.
A PARODY OF A POEM IS STILL A POEM.
A PUBLIC SQUARE STRIPPED OF EVERYTHING BUT COMMERCE -
WITH PRIVATE SECURITY
ENFORCING THE **MORES** OF COMMERCE.
PEOPLE JUST WANT A PLACE TO WALK AROUND AND DRINK SODA.
THE SAME STORES IN EVERY TOWN-
STORES FROM EVERYWHERE
EVERYWHERE!
GLOBALISM!
A PECULIAR, HOUSE-TRAINED GLOBALISM.
THERE ARE MORE THINGS IN THE FOOD COURT THAN ARE DREAMT OF IN YOUR PHILOSOPHY.

Wasteland

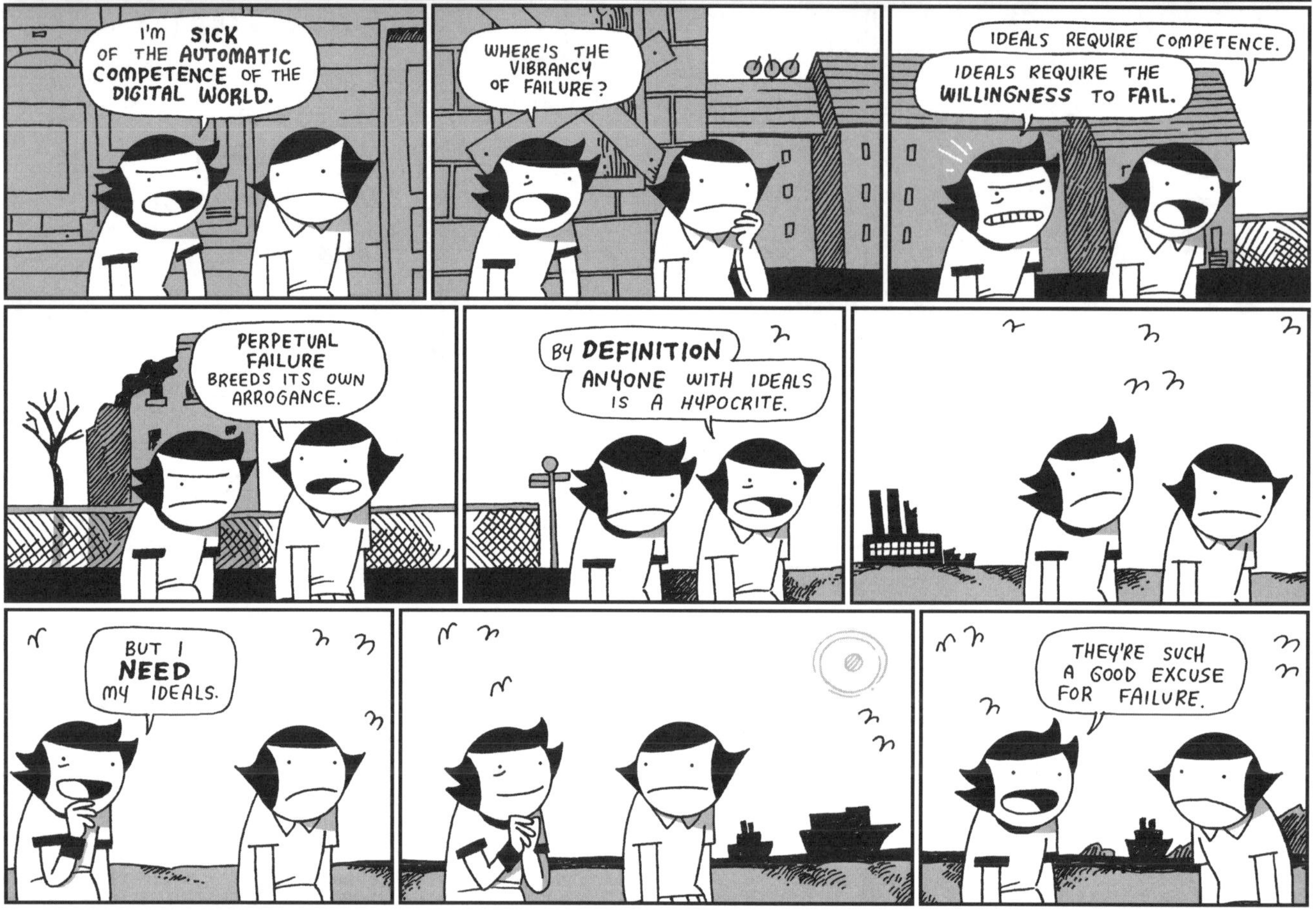
I'm SICK OF THE AUTOMATIC COMPETENCE OF THE DIGITAL WORLD.
WHERE'S THE VIBRANCY OF FAILURE?
IDEALS REQUIRE COMPETENCE.
IDEALS REQUIRE THE WILLINGNESS TO FAIL.
PERPETUAL FAILURE BREEDS ITS OWN ARROGANCE.
BY DEFINITION
ANYONE WITH IDEALS IS A HYPOCRITE.
BUT I NEED MY IDEALS.
THEY'RE SUCH A GOOD EXCUSE FOR FAILURE.

Heat Wave

A BOAT.
THE SMELL OF THE OCEAN
WIND WHIPPING THE SALT SPRAY
A COOLER FULL OF SANDWICHES AND FANTA
WATER ALL AROUND AND THE SUN FAR AWAY IN THE SKY.
I'D LIKE TO BE ON A BOAT.
WHERE WOULD YOU RATHER BE?

Light Up the Sky With My Name

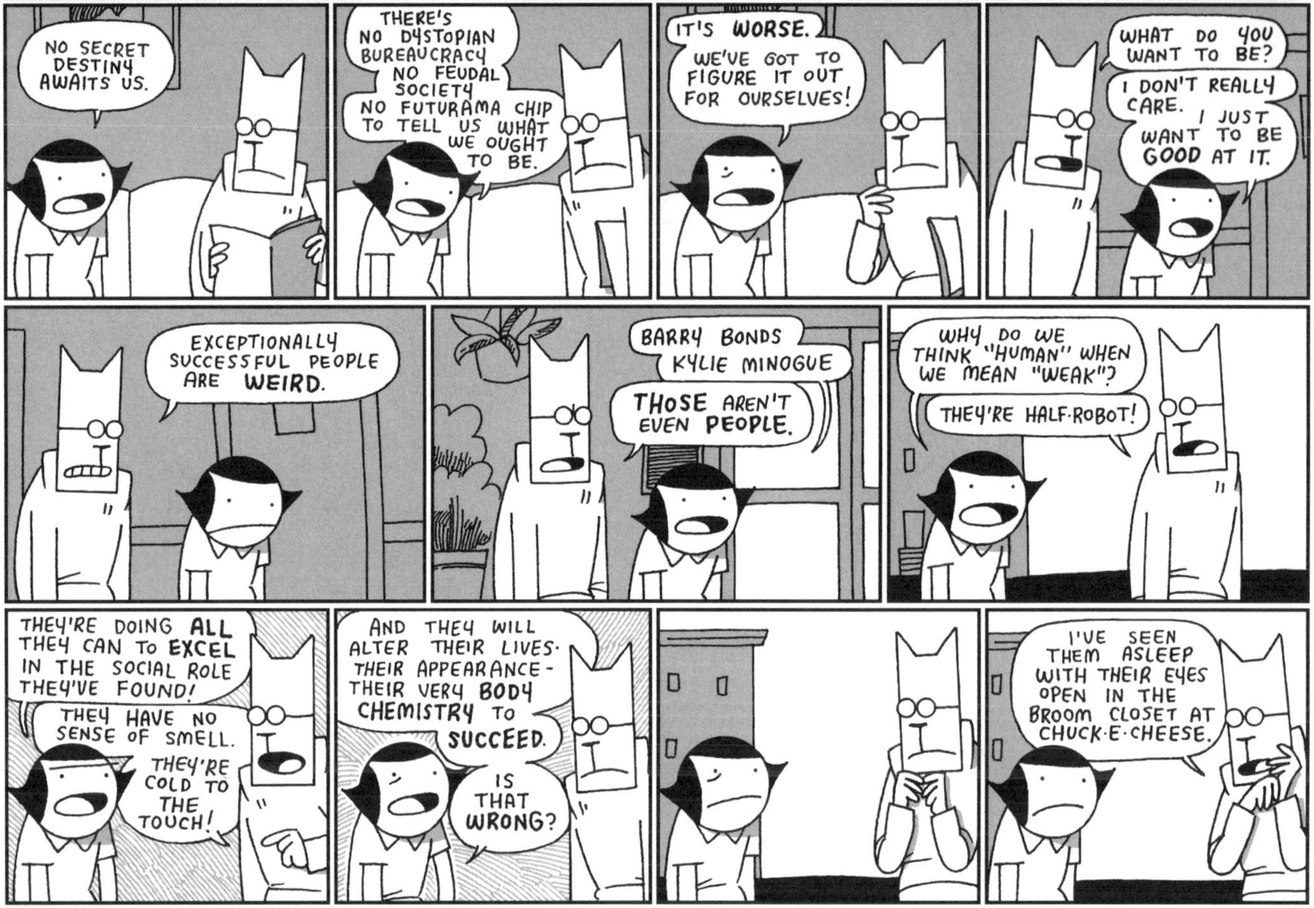
NO SECRET DESTINY AWAITS US.
THERE'S NO DYSTOPIAN BUREAUCRACY NO FEUDAL SOCIETY NO FUTURAMA CHIP TO TELL US WHAT WE OUGHT TO BE.
IT'S WORSE. WE'VE GOT TO FIGURE IT OUT FOR OURSELVES!
WHAT DO YOU WANT TO BE?
I DON'T REALLY CARE. I JUST WANT TO BE GOOD AT IT.
EXCEPTIONALLY SUCCESSFUL PEOPLE ARE WEIRD.
BARRY BONDS
KYLIE MINOGUE
THOSE AREN'T EVEN PEOPLE.
WHY DO WE THINK "HUMAN" WHEN WE MEAN "WEAK"?
THEY'RE HALF-ROBOT!
THEY'RE DOING ALL THEY CAN TO EXCEL IN THE SOCIAL ROLE THEY'VE FOUND!
THEY HAVE NO SENSE OF SMELL.
THEY'RE COLD TO THE TOUCH!
AND THEY WILL ALTER THEIR LIVES· THEIR APPEARANCE- THEIR VERY BODY CHEMISTRY TO SUCCEED.
IS THAT WRONG?
I'VE SEEN THEM ASLEEP WITH THEIR EYES OPEN IN THE BROOM CLOSET AT CHUCK·E·CHEESE.

Faith

WHO CAN BELIEVE IN THE LOCH NESS MONSTER WHEN ANTARCTICA IS OPEN TO TOURISTS?
WHEN EVERY LAST PERSON CARRIES A CELL PHONE, A CAMERA-
WHEN EVERY LAST INCH OF THIS PLANET AND OTHERS HAS BEEN MAPPED - PHOTOGRAPHED - EVALUATED AND RATED.
I WANT MYSTERY IN LIFE!
LAST WEEK-
WE NEEDED BIGFOOT TO REMIND US THAT PARTS OF THE WORLD WERE STILL UNKNOWN.
WE NEEDED TO KNOW THAT THERE WAS A WORLD WHERE HUMANS WERE INTRUDERS.
WHERE IS THE ROMANCE OF THE UNKNOWN NOW?
WHAT MYSTERY REMAINS-
WHAT'S THAT SMELL?
LAST WEEK I HID FRUIT IN THE BOOKCASE!

Pick Me Up on Your Way Down

ALCHEMY!
ONE PART BREAKS AND THE WHOLE MACHINE TURNS TO CRAP.
REPLACEMENT PARTS AVAILABLE ONLY AT YOUR AUTHORIZED REPLACEMENT PARTS DEALER
CONVENIENTLY LOCATED AT THE EXACT CENTER OF THE EARTH.
I HAPPEN TO KNOW A PORTAL TO THE EXACT CENTER OF THE EARTH!
NOBODY USE THE TOILET FOR A COUPLE OF HOURS.

The Legacy of Empire

AMERICA'S GOT NO CULTURE.
AMERICA'S GOT THE CULTURE!
NAILS
YOU CAN'T SEE IT BECAUSE IT'S UBIQUITOUS.
I DON'T MEAN THE BLUE JEANS AND HAMBURGERS DEPLOYED FOR GLOBAL CONSUMPTION-
TANNING
I MEAN THE UNIQUELY AMERICAN.
WHAT DO WE HAVE THAT IS US?
THAT IS OURS AND JUST OURS?
OUR RICH TRADITION OF PRISON RAPE JOKES?
AND SALT WATER TAFFY!

Blasphemers

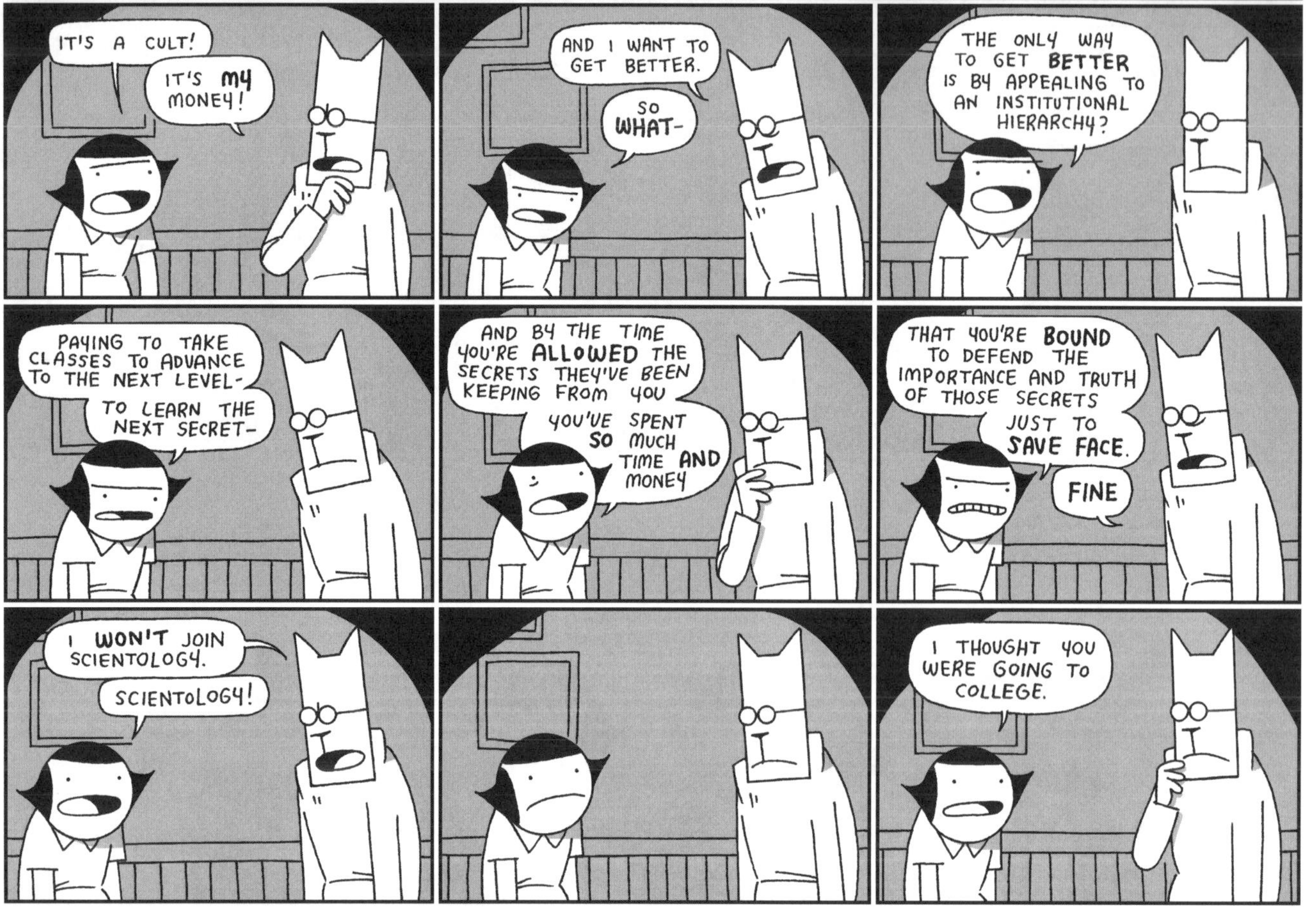
IT'S A CULT!
IT'S MY MONEY!
AND I WANT TO GET BETTER.
SO WHAT-
THE ONLY WAY TO GET BETTER IS BY APPEALING TO AN INSTITUTIONAL HIERARCHY?
PAYING TO TAKE CLASSES TO ADVANCE TO THE NEXT LEVEL-
TO LEARN THE NEXT SECRET-
AND BY THE TIME YOU'RE ALLOWED THE SECRETS THEY'VE BEEN KEEPING FROM YOU
YOU'VE SPENT SO MUCH TIME AND MONEY
THAT YOU'RE BOUND TO DEFEND THE IMPORTANCE AND TRUTH OF THOSE SECRETS
JUST TO SAVE FACE.
FINE
I WON'T JOIN SCIENTOLOGY.
SCIENTOLOGY!
I THOUGHT YOU WERE GOING TO COLLEGE.

Buffet Lines

WE'RE MOVING ON UP.
TO THE EAST SIDE?
TO THAT DELUXE APARTMENT IN THE SKY!
WE'RE MOVING ON UP
TO THE EAST SIDE
WE DON'T HAVE A DELUXE APARTMENT.
WE'VE FINALLY GOT OUR PIECE OF THE PIE!
THAT'S QUICHE.

The Way We Were

APPLES FOR SALE.
APPLES!
LUXURY.
WHAT?
THAT'S WHAT SELLS-
BOOTLEG LUXURY-
IF LUXURY MEANT QUALITY
BOOTLEG DESIGNER HANDBAGS AND SUNGLASSES WOULDN'T MAKE SENSE-
BUT WHEN LUXURY BECOMES A BRAND - AN IDEA - A LOGO-
THEN THE APPEARANCE OF LUXURY IS LUXURY.
IN A FLUSH CIVILIZATION-
SURE.
THERE'S A REASON MEDIEVAL HOLIDAYS WERE FEAST DAYS-
LUXURY THEN WAS PLENTIFUL FOOD.
ADEQUATE HEATING-
TRAVEL!-
THIS WAS LUXURY
AVAILABLE ONLY TO SOCIETY'S MOST PRIVILEGED.
LOOKS LIKE WE'RE DUE FOR A REVIVAL.
THE PART OF THE BLACK DEATH WILL BE PLAYED BY DRUG-RESISTANT TUBERCULOSIS.

ENABLER'S
2 FOR 1 TUES DAYS

Extreme Tourism

A HISTORY OF BRUTAL EXPLOITATION.
BACK WHEN IT WAS CALLED THE BELGIAN WAFFLE - THE PERSONAL PROPERTY OF KING LEOPOLD.
MANAGED FOR THE FINANCIAL GAIN OF ITS OVERSEAS OVERLORDS - EXPORTING SWEETS IMPORTING DIABETES.
AND TODAY CANDYLAND FACES THE LEGACY OF COLONIALISM-
THE STABLE BUT REPRESSIVE REGIME OF FIELD MARSHALL MALLOW-
THE RIGGED ELECTIONS- THE JAILED DISSIDENTS-
IS THAT ASPARAGUS?
YEAH-
COME WITH ME.
PLEASE.
KA CHUNK

Winners and Losers

CAN I HELP YOU WITH ANYTHING?
NO.
JUST LOOKING.
WE V
CASH ONLY
NO SH
YOU DO NEED TO BUY SOMETHING IF YOU WANT YOUR LIFE VALIDATED.
OK.
WE VALIDATE
CASH ONLY
NO SHOES
WELL THERE GOES THAT.
DID YOU WANT VALIDATION?
IS THAT A BAD THING?
I THOUGHT WE WERE IN THIS TOGETHER!
AGAINST LIFE AS THE EXCHANGE OF FREE WILL FOR A PAYCHECK- SUCCESS AS HOW MUCH MONEY YOU MAKE AND THE STATUS OF OBJECTS AND EXPERIENCES YOU SPEND THAT MONEY ON-
IF IT'S MONEY-
IT'S NOT JUST MONEY!
THERE ARE OTHER ARBITRARY HIERARCHIES CATERING TO OUR SICK DRIVE FOR VALIDITY IN THE EYES OF SOCIETY.
I'M GOING INTO ACADEMIA!

First Things First

HOO!
WHO?
US.
WHERE?
HOO!
WHAT?
WAT...
OK!
WE'RE GOING TO ANGKOR WAT!
WHERE'S WHAT?
WAT HAPPENED-
WHAT HAPPENED TO WHO?
HOO'S NOWHERE NEAR WAT.
WHO'S GOING?
SUTTON HOO ISN'T GOING ANYWHERE!
FINE!
YOU DECIDE WHERE WE'RE GOING.
NO.
THE THEATER IT IS!

WHAT'S IN THE REFRIGERATOR?
MARGARITA MIX.
WHAT'S IN THE BATHTUB?
GIN.
WHAT'S IN THE TOILET?
SLOPPY JOES.
NO ONE IS COMING TO OUR PARTY.

TWO HAMBURGERS.
ANY TOPPINGS?
CAN I GET CHEESE?
THAT'S FORTY CENTS EXTRA.
FRIED ONIONS?
TWENTY CENTS.
MAYONNAISE?
TEN CENTS.
PICKLES?
A QUARTER.
WHAT CAN I GET FOR **FREE**?
FOOD POISONING.
DON'T YOU LIKE A BARGAIN?

WHAT DO YOU CALL A LOLLIPOP WITH PRINCIPLES?
A SUCKER.

WHAT IF I TRY AND TRY
AND IT NEVER GETS BETTER?
THE CERTAINTY THAT ONE DAY **THIS WILL BE WORTH IT**-
IT EBBS AND FLOWS.
OR ONE DAY THAT TIDE WILL LEAVE AND IT WILL **NEVER** COME BACK.
AND I'LL WAKE UP AND THINK
ALL THAT TIME I SPENT
WORKING ON MY **NOVEL**
I COULD HAVE BEEN TAKING BETTER CARE OF MY TEETH.
I COULD HAVE BEEN LEARNING TO **INVEST**.
I COULD HAVE SPENT MY SATURDAYS WALKING AMONG WATERFALLS IN HIGH CLASS SHOPPING CENTERS-
COMPARING TRIFLE DISHES AT CRATE AND BARREL AND TRYING ON CASHMERE SWEATERS EMBROIDERED WITH DUCKS IN FLIGHT.
THOSE ARE SOME DEEP-SEATED INSECURITIES.
HAVE YOU TALKED TO PEOPLE WITH SHALLOWLY-SEATED INSECURITIES?
A-N-N-O-Y-I-N-G.

COFFEE
BEER
GEORGE RUSSELL SAID-
A LITERARY SCENE IS "FIVE OR SIX MEN WHO LIVE IN THE SAME TOWN AND HATE EACH OTHER."
A SCENE IS A ROOM FULL OF PEOPLE WITH THE SAME VENEREAL DISEASE.

EVERYONE LOVES SILLY STRAWS.
IT'S A GREAT IDEA!
I AM GOING TO MAKE A MILLION DOLLARS!
IT'S A TERRIBLE IDEA.
NOBODY WANTS A SILLY CATHETER.

A Day at the Races

WHAT ARE THE GREYHOUNDS CHASING?
DISSATISFACTION.
WHY?
I'D RATHER
DON'T YOU EVER LOOK BACK ON THINGS YOU MADE A FEW YEARS AGO
I'D RATHER HAVE GOOD + PLENTY.
AND FEEL DISSATISFIED?
BUT WHAT OPTION IS THERE?
UGH.
TO BE SATISFIED WITH THE PAST IS TO BE MOVING IN THE WRONG DIRECTION-
OR WORSE-
SATISFACTION IS COMPLACENCY IS STASIS.
IS THAT WHY THEY RUN SO FAST?
THEY DON'T KNOW IT'S DISSATISFACTION UNTIL THEY REACH IT.
THEY NEVER REACH IT.
LUCKY DOGS.

BAD DECISION DINOSAUR GOES ON HOLIDAY

SPF

GREYHOUND
OPEN
YHOUND

Greek to Me

WE CAN SPEND OUR LIVES ALWAYS SEEKING
WANTING
MORE
OR WE CAN BE SATISFIED WITH WHAT WE'VE GOT.
WHICH IS THE GREATER TRAGEDY?
YOU MAKE EVERYTHING SAD.
DO YOU HAVE A BEST FRIEND?
LET'S DO SOMETHING FUN.
I LIKE FUN.
LET'S HAVE A POOL PARTY!
I'LL RENT DIABOLIQUE!

Hindsight

REMEMBER WHEN PEOPLE SOLD OUT?
THE CONCEPT'S NOT EVEN RELEVANT ANY MORE.
HOW CAN IT BE WHEN IT DESCRIBES EVERYONE?
IF THE INTERNET WORKS AGAINST THE PURITY OF AN UNDERGROUND-
IT WORKS AGAINST EXCLUSIVITY TOO.
LUST FOR LIFE IN A COMMERCIAL FOR ROYAL CARIBBEAN CRUISE LINES!
A SONG THAT CELEBRATES LIFE ON THE MARGINS OF SOCIETY.
THAT SONG'S A BUNCH OF DUDES MAKING NOISE ABOUT HOW TOUGH THEY ARE!
THERE'S MORE BRUTAL HONESTY IN THE FOOD LION JINGLE.
BEING APPROPRIATED BY A FAMILY-SAFE PLEASURE CRUISE TO THE COLONIES OF THE TRAVEL INDUSTRY, BUFFET LINES AND OTHER PEOPLE'S STICKY CHILDREN WAS THE BEST THING THAT COULD HAVE HAPPENED TO IT!
LUST FOR LIFE IS NOT ABOUT GOOD TIMES!
HAVE YOU BEEN ON A CRUISE?

HELP.
HELP!
HELP HELP HELP
OVER HERE!
USS SOCIAL SINKING
BRAVO!
CHAMPAGNE FOR EVERYONE.
ACHOO!
I DON'T FEEL SO GOOD.
HOT CHAMPAGNE FOR THE GIRL.
HOLD ON-
YANK
TIK TIK TIK
THE DOCTOR SAYS TAKE ANTIBIOTICS
WE STILL HAVE AFFORDABLE HEALTH CARE!
YANK
TIK TIK TIK
THE DOCTOR SAYS ANTI DEPRESSANTS
TIK TIK YANK TIK TIK TIK TIK
TIK TIK
THE DOCTOR SAYS SEE A SPECIALIST
KAF KAF KAF
DO YOU HAVE A MAGIC EIGHT BALL?

YANK
TIK TIK TIK TIK TIK
THE DOCTOR SAYS
STAND ON AN ICE FLOE AND WAVE GOODBYE TO YOUR FAMILY
YANK
TIK TIK TIK TIK
THE DOCTOR SAYS
STAND ON AN ICE FLOE AND
YANK
TIK
TIK TIK
THE DOCTOR SAYS
STAND ON AN ICE FLOE AND
WHERE AM I GOING TO GET AN ICE FLOE?
U.S.S. HUBRIS
THE U.S.S. GLOBAL WARMING WILL SAVE US.

Commodities

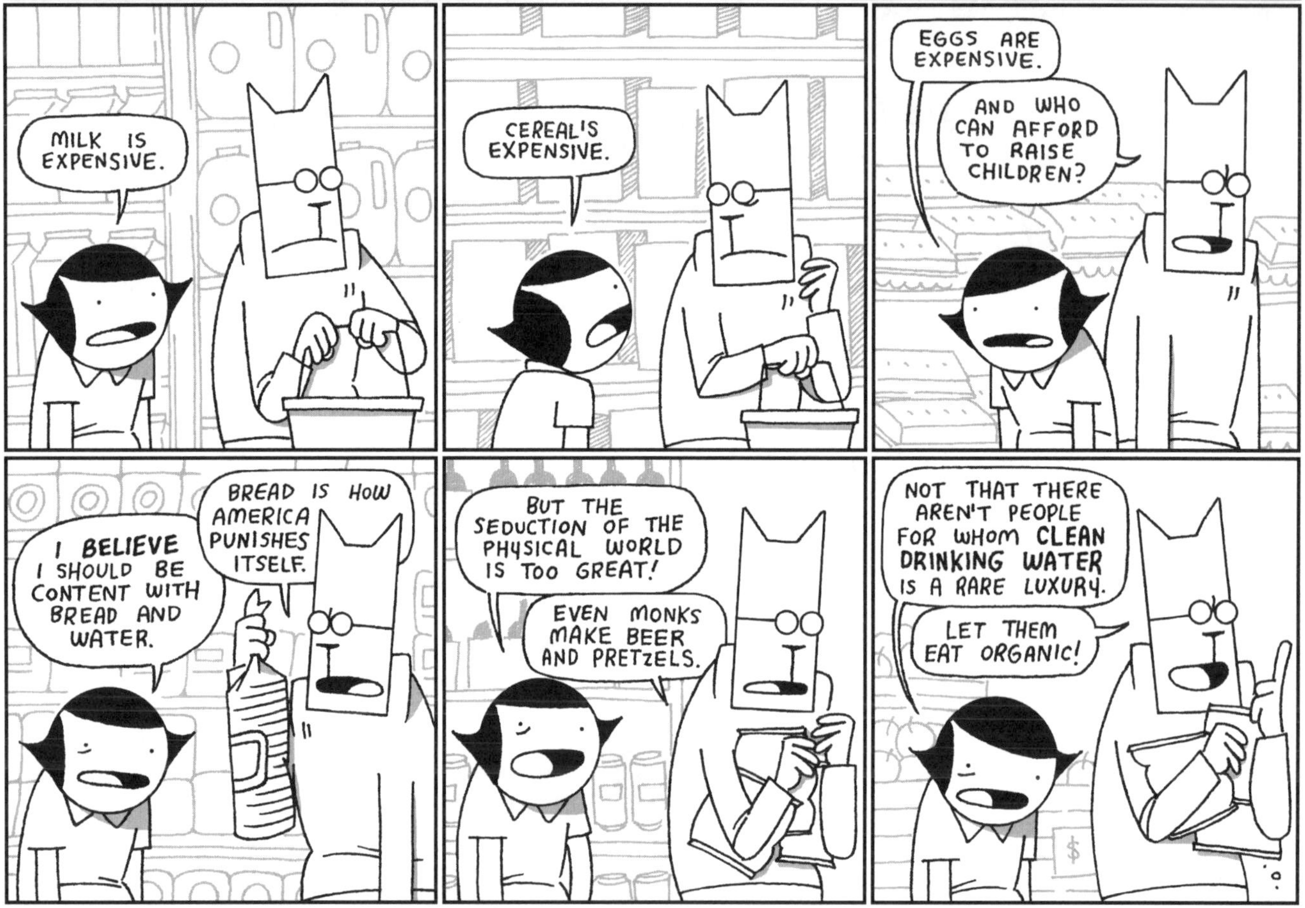

MILK IS EXPENSIVE.
CEREAL'S EXPENSIVE.
EGGS ARE EXPENSIVE.
AND WHO CAN AFFORD TO RAISE CHILDREN?
I BELIEVE I SHOULD BE CONTENT WITH BREAD AND WATER.
BREAD IS HOW AMERICA PUNISHES ITSELF.
BUT THE SEDUCTION OF THE PHYSICAL WORLD IS TOO GREAT!
EVEN MONKS MAKE BEER AND PRETZELS.
NOT THAT THERE AREN'T PEOPLE FOR WHOM CLEAN DRINKING WATER IS A RARE LUXURY.
LET THEM EAT ORGANIC!

Living Alone

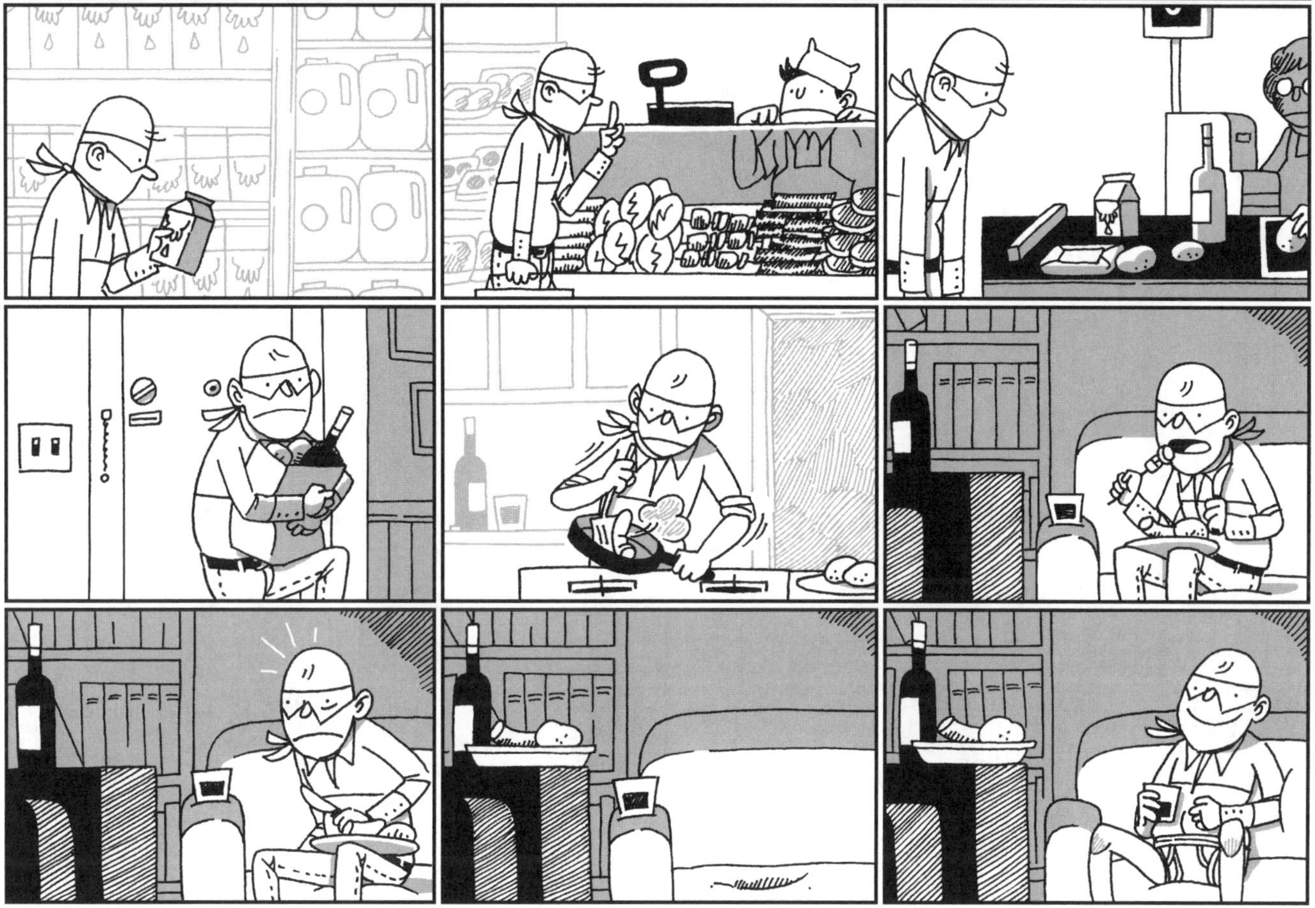

Ghosts

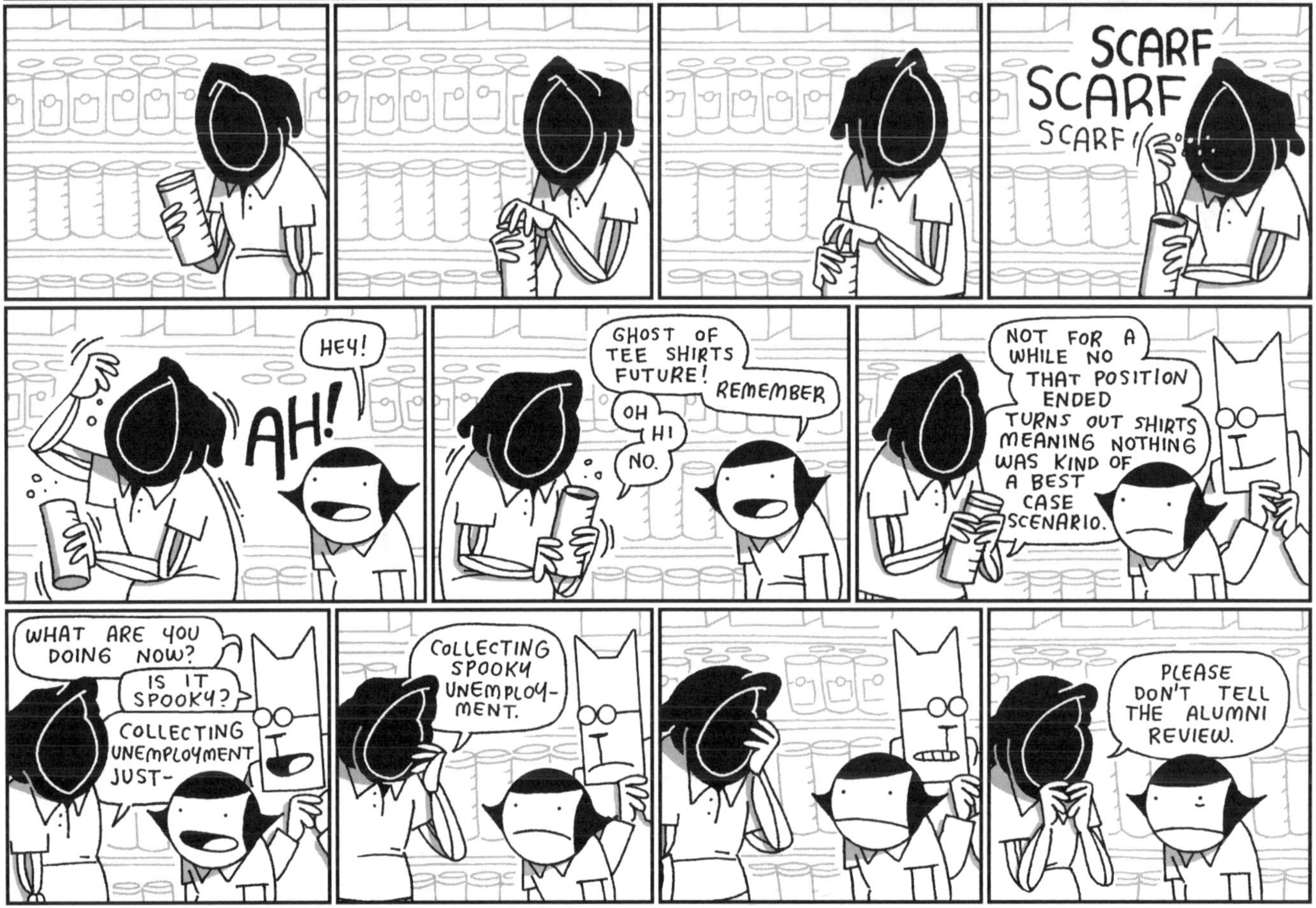

SCARF
SCARF
SCARF
HEY!
AH!
GHOST OF TEE SHIRTS FUTURE!
REMEMBER
OH
HI
NO.
NOT FOR A WHILE NO THAT POSITION ENDED
TURNS OUT SHIRTS MEANING NOTHING WAS KIND OF A BEST CASE SCENARIO.
WHAT ARE YOU DOING NOW?
IS IT SPOOKY?
COLLECTING UNEMPLOYMENT JUST-
COLLECTING SPOOKY UNEMPLOY-MENT.
PLEASE DON'T TELL THE ALUMNI REVIEW.

YOU KNOW WALTER BENJAMIN'S THEORY OF TRANSLATION.
I LIKE ARCADES.
A TRANSPARENT RESTATEMENT OF MEANING IS UNTRUE TO ITS SOURCE.
INKY
BLINKY
PINKY
AND
ANY TEE SHIRT'S STATED MEANING SHOULD BE UNDERSTOOD AS FOREIGN
SUE!
MY LAW FIRM!
MAINTAINING THE TENSION BETWEEN WHAT WE PERCEIVE AS MEANING AND THE EXISTENCE OF MEANING IN A PLACE BEYOND OUR UNDER-STANDING.
HOW DO YOU LIKE YOUR LAW?
FIRM.
LIKE IN MANDARIN POP.
OR TEAM HANDBALL.
HOW DO YOU LIKE YOUR LEGAL?
TENDER
SO TENDER
TUMBLE
GASP
GASP
GASP
DID YOU CHANGE YOUR SHIRT?

THAT'S NOT YOU?!
WHO IS IT?
!?
A STRANGER.
A DOPPEL-GANGER!
NO
NO
I DON'T THINK YOU'RE TALLER.
MAYBE JUST A LITTLE BIT.

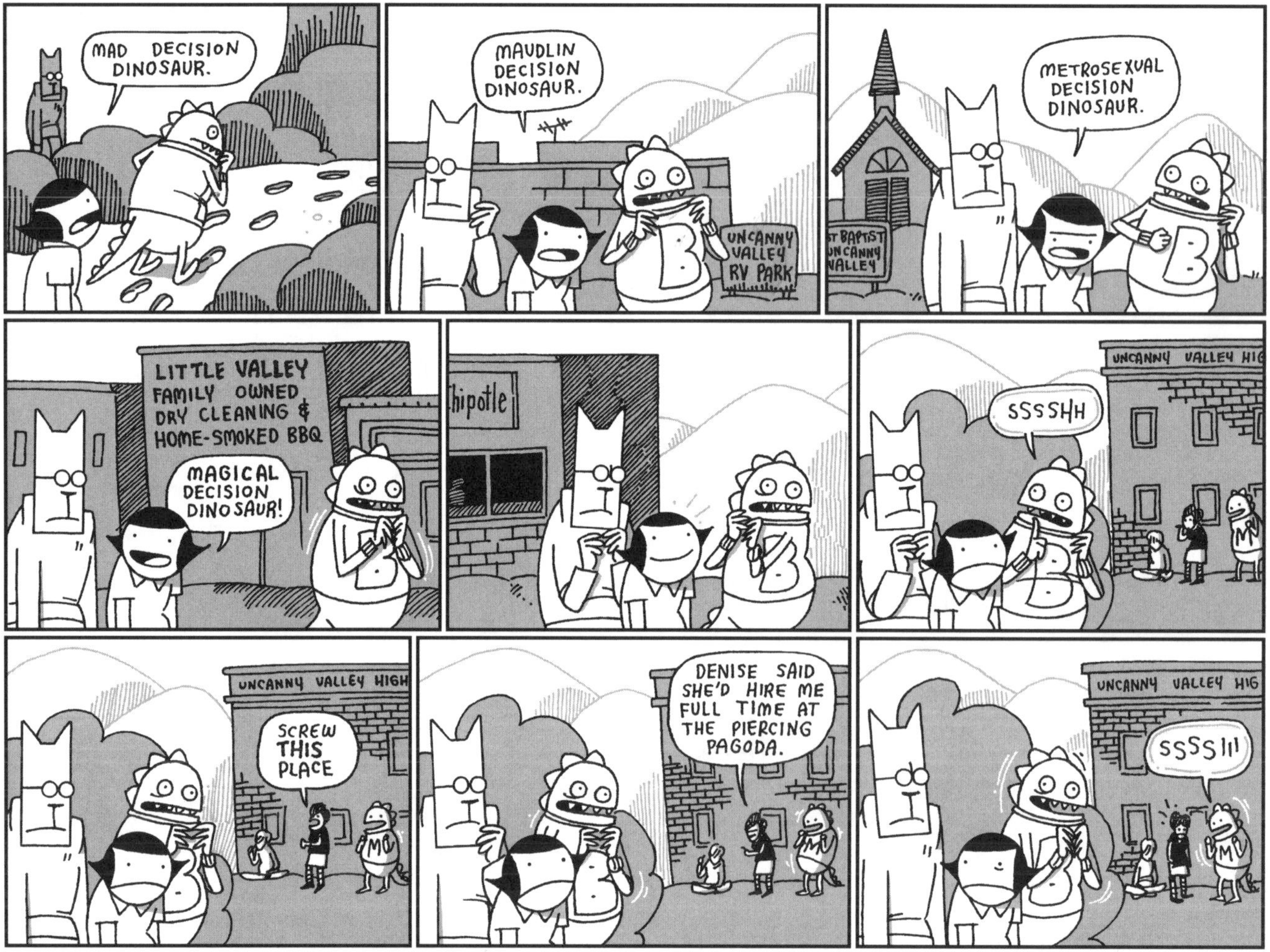
MAD DECISION DINOSAUR.
MAUDLIN DECISION DINOSAUR.
UNCANNY VALLEY RV PARK
METROSEXUAL DECISION DINOSAUR.
ST BAPTIST UNCANNY VALLEY
LITTLE VALLEY FAMILY OWNED DRY CLEANING & HOME-SMOKED BBQ
MAGICAL DECISION DINOSAUR!
Chipotle
UNCANNY VALLEY HIG
SSSSHH
UNCANNY VALLEY HIGH
SCREW THIS PLACE
DENISE SAID SHE'D HIRE ME FULL TIME AT THE PIERCING PAGODA.
UNCANNY VALLEY HIG
SSSSHH

MALA DECISIÓN DINOSAURIO!
BAD!
SNIFF
WHILE
WHEN YOU'RE WORKING AT THE MALL I'M GONNA
I'M GONNA FINISH HIGH SCHOOL AND GO TO COLLEGE AND GET A JOB AND SAVE MONEY AND BUY A HOUSE AND SHOP AT CRATE AND BARREL AND INVEST FOR MY RETIREMENT!
YESSSSS
SSSSIIIII

Wheels within Wheels

I CAN'T BRING MYSELF TO BELIEVE IN A FUTURE.
DO YOU
SSSSHHH! MY SHOW'S ON!
CLICK CLICK
WELCOME BACK TO
WHEEL OF ENTROPY!
WITH YOUR HOST ONE HUNDRED AND FORTY POUNDS OF ROTTING BANANAS!
GO ON CHUCK
GIVE THAT WHEEL A SPIN!
TIK TIK TIK TIK TIK TIK TIK TIK
CLUNK
WE LIVE IN A WORLD WITHOUT FORTUNE.
NO!
WAIT
HOLD ON
CRACK
"HOPE FOR LESS."

Abstract Expressionist

FAZOOM!!
THUD
VROWRR
SCREEEEEEE
CRASH!
THERE IS NO ONE LINE SEPARATING PLAN FROM ACCIDENT.

Drug of Choice

NO THANKS
I PREFER SELF-RIGHTEOUSNESS.

Fractions

WHAT IS WORSE THAN FINDING A WORM IN YOUR APPLE?
HALF A WORM.
A QUARTER OF A WORM?
A TINY HAT AND SUITCASE
AND A NOTE THAT SAYS "GOODBYE WORLD?"

Hysteria

ONE OUT OF FIVE ARMCHAIR DOCTORS AGREE
MENTAL ILLNESS IS A SOCIAL CONSTRUCT!
OF COURSE
WE LOOK TO SOCIETY FOR GUIDANCE IN HOW TO EXPRESS OURSELVES.
TWO OUT OF SEVEN ARMCHAIRS AGREE
AUGH GET OFF
GET OFF
AND DIAGNOSES GO IN AND OUT OF VOGUE LIKE DIET FADS
ONE DAY IT'S A.D.D.
THE NEXT IT'S HIKIKOMORI
THREE OUT OF SEVEN ARMCHAIRS SAY
GET OUT MORE-LEARN TO GARDEN!
BUT IF DIAGNOSIS IS SOCIETY'S WAY OF UNDERSTANDING WHAT IS WRONG INSIDE US
THAT WRONGNESS IS STILL REAL.
ONE OUT OF EVERY SEVEN ARMCHAIRS WANTS TO KNOW WHY YOU ONLY USE THE LIVING ROOM WHEN COMPANY COMES OVER
AND WE'RE ALL WRONG INSIDE-
BUT ONLY SOME OF US ARE CALLED ILL.
MENTAL ILLNESS ISN'T THE SOCIAL CONSTRUCT
MENTAL WELLNESS IS.
AND THE LAST ARMCHAIR WONDERS WHERE IS HIS MOTHER
DOES SHE EVEN REMEMBER

Wheremones

SNIFF
SNIFF
SNIFF
ARE YOU WEARING COLOGNE?
IT'S PEANUT BUTTER!

Attention Shoppers
PSSSSST
IT'S MY SECRET IDENTITY!
FOR WHAT
FOR WHAT
FOR EVERYTHING
THERE'S NO PRIVACY IN SOCIETY
OUR EVERY MOVE IS RECORDED BY CREDIT CARD AND EZ PASS
YOU CAN'T GO OUTSIDE WITHOUT ENDING UP ON A SURVEILLANCE CAMERA OR TAGGED IN A PHOTO ON FACEBOOK!
A SECRET IDENTITY IS THE ONLY RESPONSE LEFT
A SECRET IDENTITY-
OH
OH
I HAVE MY SHOPRITE CLUB CARD.
BEEP
WELCOME GRRRL
I NEED THE SAVINGS.

Our Candidate

EXCUSE ME
EXCUSE ME
OVER HERE
HOW WOULD YOU ADDRESS OVERCROWDING IN THE PRISON SYSTEM?
TOURING PRODUCTIONS OF GODSPELL.
THE RISING UNEMPLOYMENT RATE-
HIGH SCHOOL IS NOW EIGHT YEARS LONG.
ABORTION?
ONLY WHEN REQUESTED.
HOME FORECLOSURES
NOW IS A GOOD TIME TO START YOUR ARTS COLONY IN AN ABANDONED SUBDIVISION OUTSIDE OF PHOENIX.
BUT THE VICTIMS OF NINJA LOANS
THROW IN SOME DINOSAUR LOANS AND MAYBE THE INTERNET WILL CARE.
IMMIGRATION-
OUR FALTERING ECONOMY WILL DISCOURAGE PEOPLE FROM COMING HERE TO MAKE A BETTER LIFE FOR THEMSELVES!
WOO!
GAS PRICES AND RENEWABLE-
PUBLIC TRANSPORTATION DISCOUNTS FOR ANYONE IN FORMAL WEAR!
HEALTH CARE.
A SINGLE-PAYER SYSTEM FOCUSED ON PREVENTATIVE MEDICINE?
DON'T BE RIDICULOUS!

JOHN KERRY.
WOAH.
FEUDALISM IS A PRETTY CLEAR EXCHANGE
DID MY WATCH STOP?
SUBJECTS TRADE AUTONOMY FOR PROTECTION-
OR ARE WE GOING TO
THE RULER'S AUTHORITY LIES IN HIS ABILITY TO PROVIDE THAT PROTECTION.
THE ELECTION 2004 THEME RESTAURANT!
TIK
TIK TIIK
AN OLIGARCHY TOO
RECOGNIZES THAT PRIVILEGE COMES WITH OBLIGATIONS-
TRY THE BEEF!
NOBLESSE OBLIGE-
WHEN YOUR COUNTRY GOES TO WAR YOU VOLUNTEER TO LEAD THE FIGHT-
LINES ARE LONG
BUT SERVICE IS SWIFT!
RIK TIK TIK
WORLD WAR I - THE DECIMATION OF THE SONS OF BRITAIN'S UPPER CLASS-
JOHN KERRY IN VIETNAM.
UNLESS YOU LIVE IN OHIO.
RIK TIK TIK TIK TIK TIK TIK TIK
IN OUR MIXED OLIGARCHY-MERITOCRACY THOSE AWARDED ADVANTAGES BY BIRTH BELIEVE THOSE ADVANTAGES TO BE EARNED AND BELIEVE THEMSELVES EXEMPT FROM OBLIGATION.
THEN YOU MIGHT JUST BE TURNED AWAY.
GEORGE BUSH IN
NOT QUITE
VIETNAM.
FIND OSAMA BIN LADEN IN THE BALL PIT AND WIN A TOY BANANA!

EVERYONE'S OUT FOR THEMSELVES
CASHING IN BONUSES AND FLEEING THE SCENE
SECURING THEIR ADVANTAGE **AGAINST** THE HOI POLLOI
RATHER THAN **FOR** IT.
AND IF SOCIETY **FAILS** SO **BE** IT!
WHAT'S THIS GOT TO DO WITH ME?
WHEE?

Sand Mansions

I JUST HAD THE ROOF REDONE.
AND THE NEW FOUR CAR GARAGE SHOULD IMPROVE THE RESALE VALUE.
PLUS I'VE GOT A COUPLE THOUSAND SAND DOLLARS IN THE BANK.
SAND DOLLARS ARE AT AN ALL-TIME LOW AGAINST THE EURO.
I THOUGHT THE MIGHTY OCEAN WOULD PROTECT ME.
POSEIDON HAD TO BUY A CONTROLLING INTEREST IN THE BANKS TO ENSURE LIQUIDITY.
CRASH
I GUESS I'M SLEEPING IN MY SAND CAR FROM NOW ON.

Join the Club

I MADE KOOL-AID.
I MADE KOOL-AID.
I MADE KOOL-AID!
WANT SOME KOOL-AID?
COLD FRESH KOOL-AID?
NO THANKS.
SO NOW YOU'RE TOO GOOD FOR A DEATH CULT?
I'M TRYING TO EAT LOCAL.

THERE ARE INFINITE WORLDS.
THE CASSINGLE MUST BE VIABLE SOMEWHERE.

The Making of a Cat and Girl Cartoon

A TWO CD SET FEATURING SOME OF NPR'S
FUNNIEST DRIVEWAY MOMENTS
HERE IN THE UNITED STATES
FIVE MEN GO ON TRIAL TODAY.
THEY'RE ALL MUSLIMS, THEY'RE ALL IN THEIR TWENTIES, AND THEY ALL LIVED IN THE PHILADELPHIA AREA
AT THE TIME THE U.S. GOVERNMENT SAID THEY WERE INVOLVED IN A TERRORIST PLOT
TO ATTACK SOLDIERS AT FORT DIX IN NEW JERSEY
CLICK
WHAT HAVE I DONE?

Pardon My French

UGH
IS IT EVEN **POSSIBLE** TO BE PART OF A CULTURE WHEN YOU'RE **SO** ALIENATED BY ITS IDEALS?
LUXURY WITHOUT QUALITY.
BIG CARS
BIG HOUSES
BIG FLAT SCREENED TVS.
HOW **NOUVEAU RICHE**.
PBR?
HOW **NOUVEAU PAUVRE**.

Lifestyles of the Nouveau Pauvre

RICE AND BEANS.
LAUNDROMATS.
TAKING FURNITURE FROM THE GARBAGE.
HAND ME DOWN VCRS.
MOVIES FROM THE LIBRARY.
TAKING KETCHUP FROM McDON-ALDS.
STEALING TOILET PAPER FROM BARS.
FREEZING IN THE WINTER.
EARNING LESS THAN YOU PAID IN COLLEGE TUITION.
DON'T MAJOR IN ENGLISH NEXT TIME.
COLLEGE WAS ONE COURSE.
UPPER MIDDLE CLASS SOCIALIZATION.
128 CREDITS.
HOW DID YOU DO?
NOT WELL.

Fear Street

SMOKEY!
BEAR STEARNS.
YOU'RE-
HANK PAULSON!
I'M THE ECONOMY.
I'M SEVEN HUNDRED BILLION DOLLARS!
IS ANYONE NOT DRESSED UP AS THE GLOBAL FINANCIAL CRISIS?
I COULDN'T AFFORD A COSTUME.

BAD DECISION DINOSAUR IN: TRICK OR TREAT!

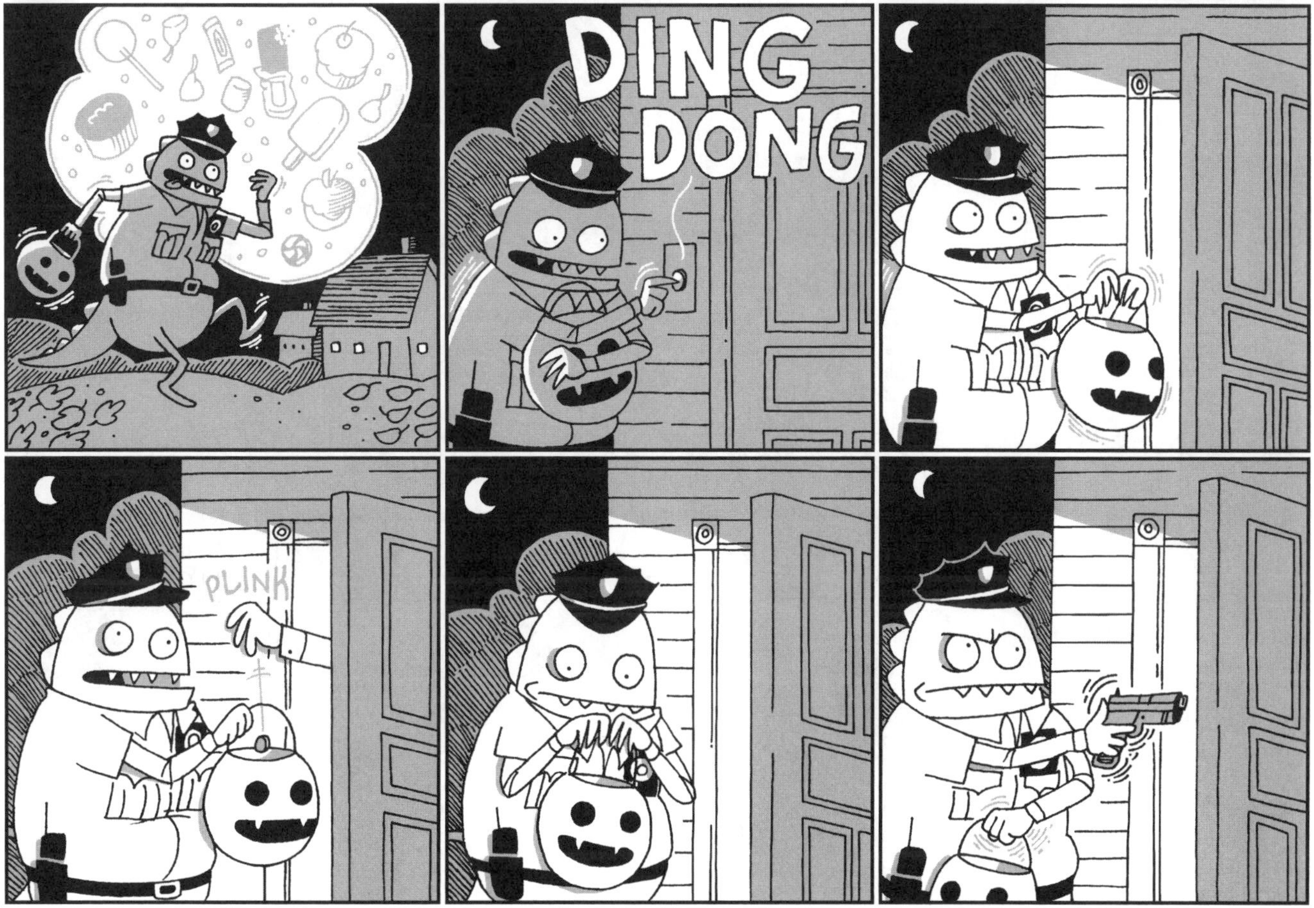
DING
DONG
PLINK

Your 2008 Presidential Election Drinking Game

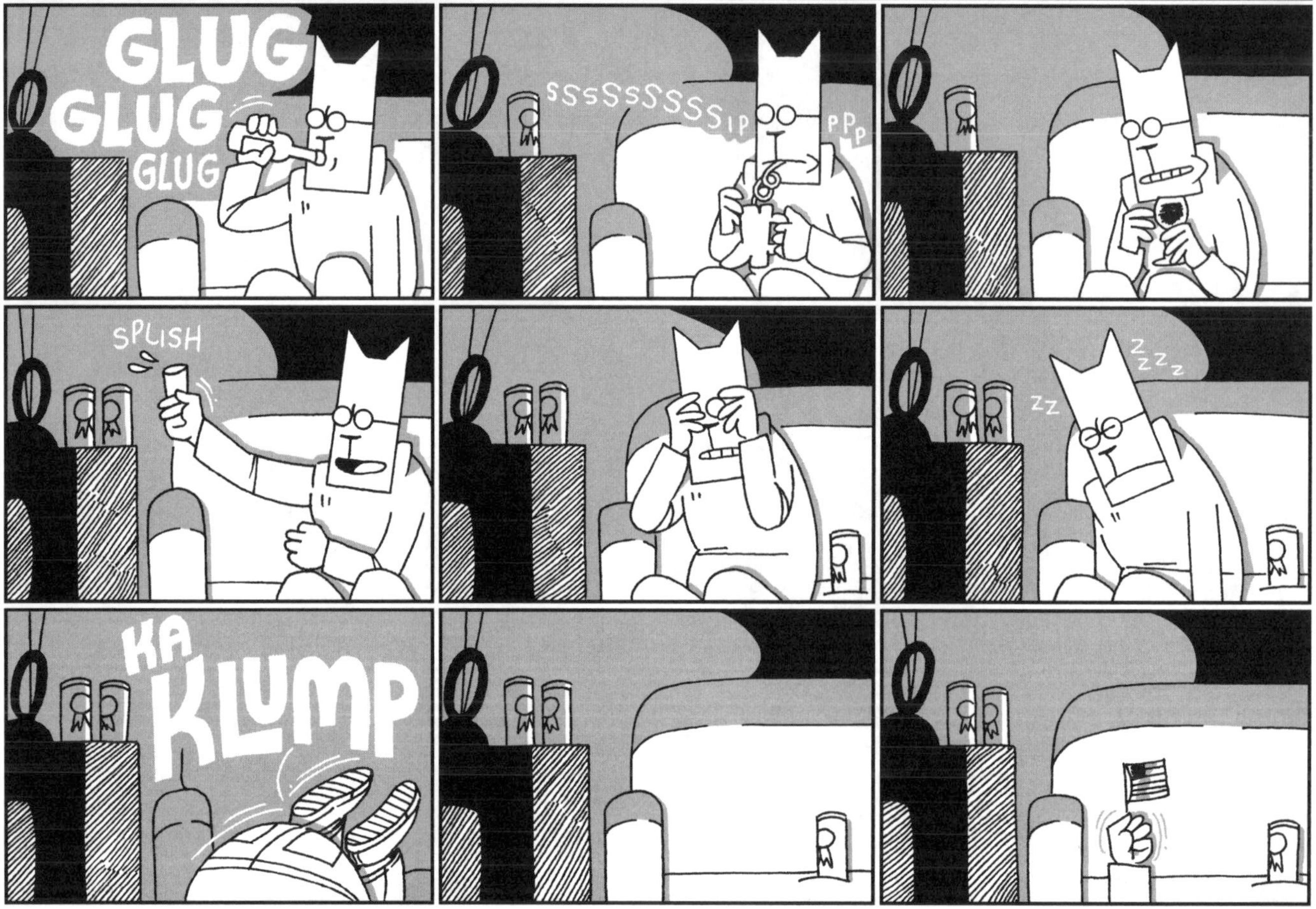
GLUG
GLUG
GLUG
SSSSSSSSSSSIP
PPP
SPLISH
ZZZZ
ZZ
KA
KLUMP

Morning in America

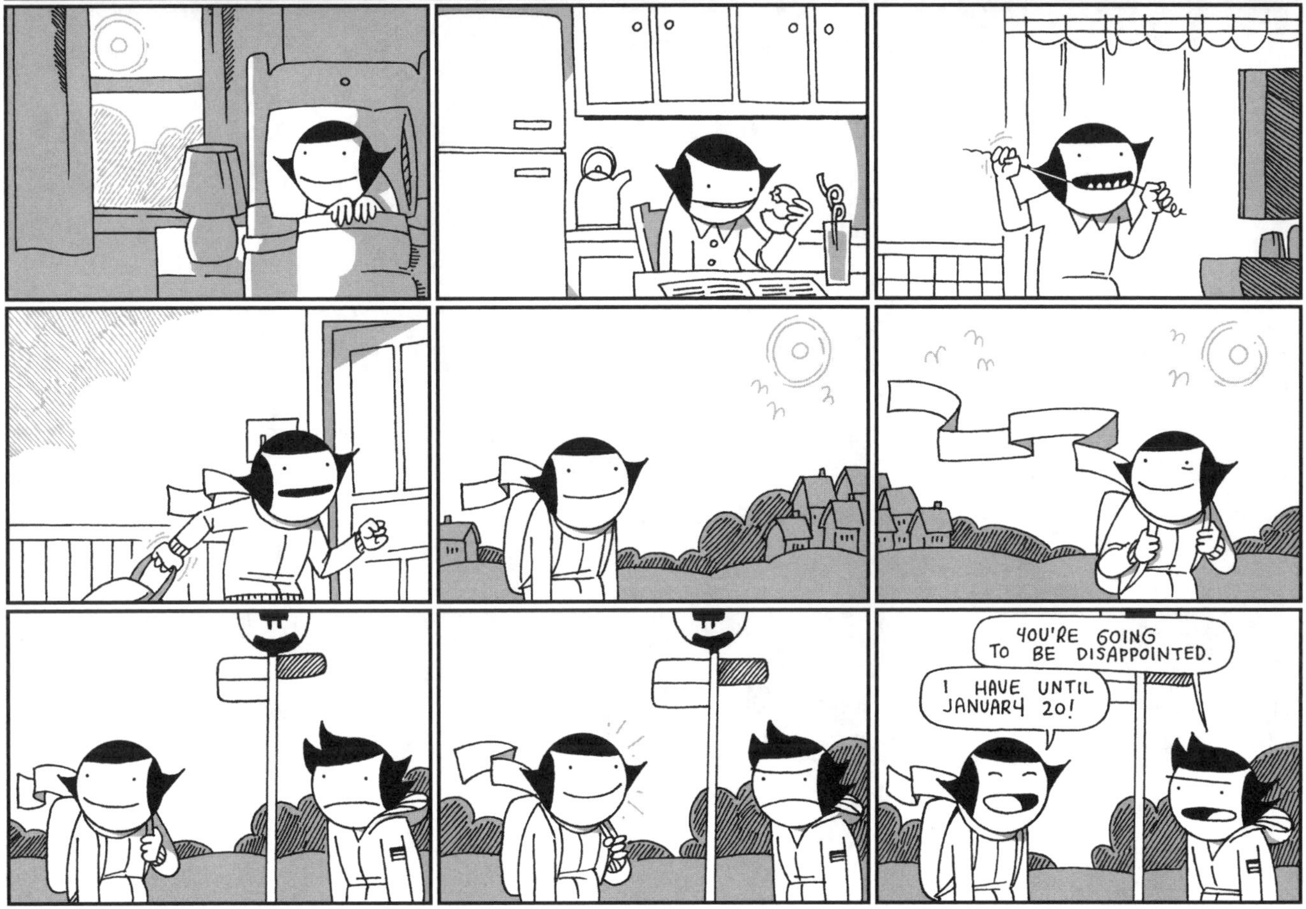
YOU'RE GOING TO BE DISAPPOINTED.
I HAVE UNTIL JANUARY 20!

Graveyard Shift
HHHOOOOO
DO YOU BELIEVE IN GHOSTS?
DO I BELIEVE IN GHOSTS?
I BELIEVE IN NOTHING SAVE THE FUTILITY OF LIFE AND THE INEVITABILITY OF DEATH.
AND WEREWOLVES.

Party Trick

LET'S GET SOME FOOD.
SURE- WHERE?
THERE'S A FARMER'S MARKET-
YUPPIES!
SELF-SATISFIED CREATIVE PROFESSIONALS PATTING THEMSELVES ON THE BACK FOR BUYING ORGANIC-
NO-
FOR BUYING LOCAL-
ORGANIC'S FOR HOCKEY MOMS AT WALMART NOW! GREEN IS THE NEW WAY TO FEEL MORALLY SUPERIOR TO THOSE WITH LESS MONEY- WITHOUT, YOU KNOW, PUTTING IT THAT WAY.
PEOPLE WITH JOBS-
PEOPLE WITH JOBS. HOW EASY IS THAT? TITHE FORTY HOURS A WEEK AND YOU GET FOOD TO EAT AND A PLACE TO SLEEP AND YOU NEVER HAVE TO SEE THE INSIDE OF A LAUNDROMAT AGAIN!
I-
YOU? A HOUSEPET?!?
YOU HAVE NO PRIVACY WHEN YOU CRAP BUT OTHERWISE IT'S SMOOTH SAILING ON SOMEONE ELSES' DIME.
ENDANGERED SPECIES.
OH LIKE THERE'S ANYONE LOOKING OUT FOR ME.
YOU CAN TWIST ANYTHING INTO RESENTMENT.
I USED TO MAKE BALLOON ANIMALS.

Limitless Possibility

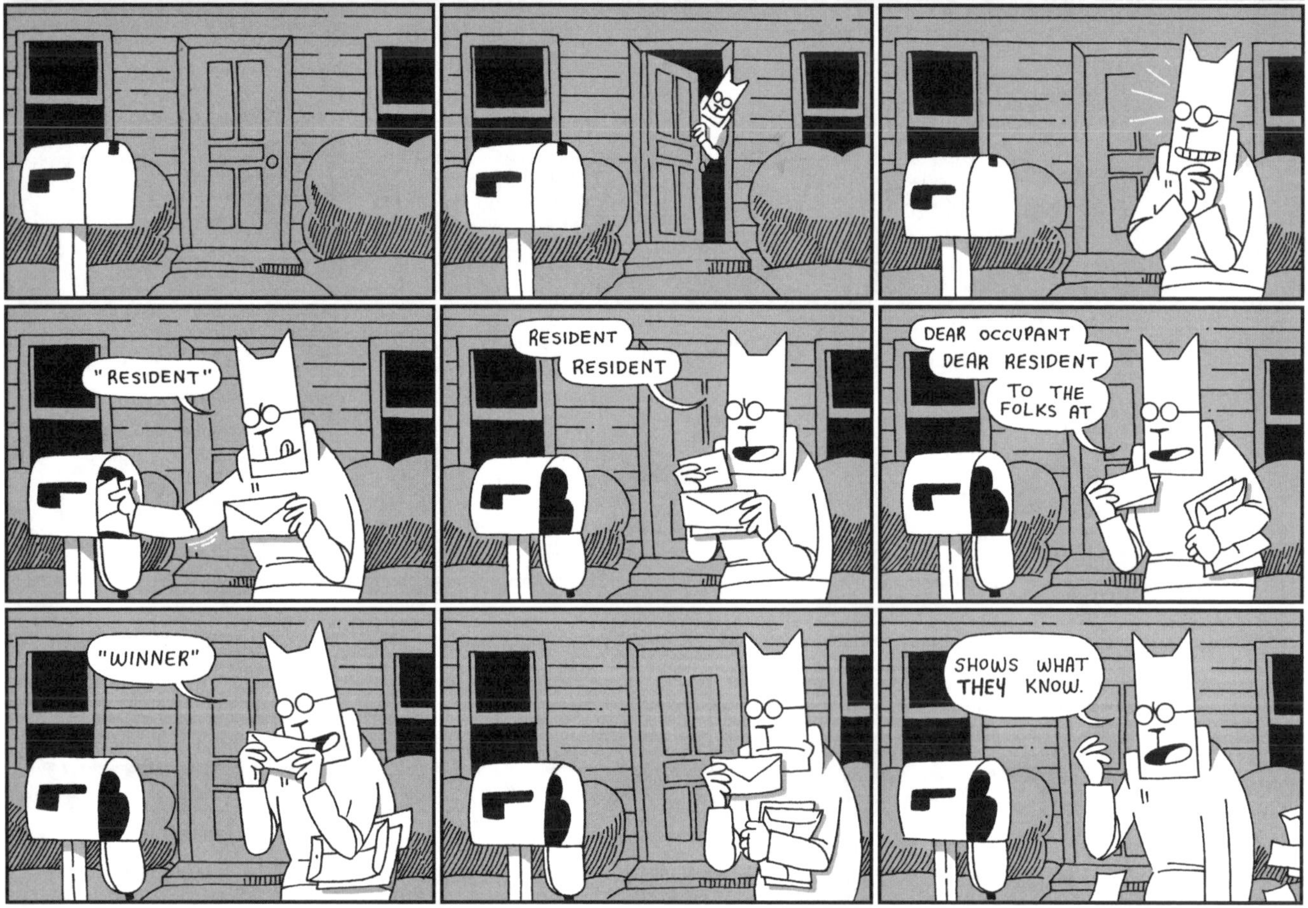
"RESIDENT"
RESIDENT
RESIDENT
DEAR OCCUPANT
DEAR RESIDENT
TO THE FOLKS AT
"WINNER"
SHOWS WHAT THEY KNOW.

Happily Ever After

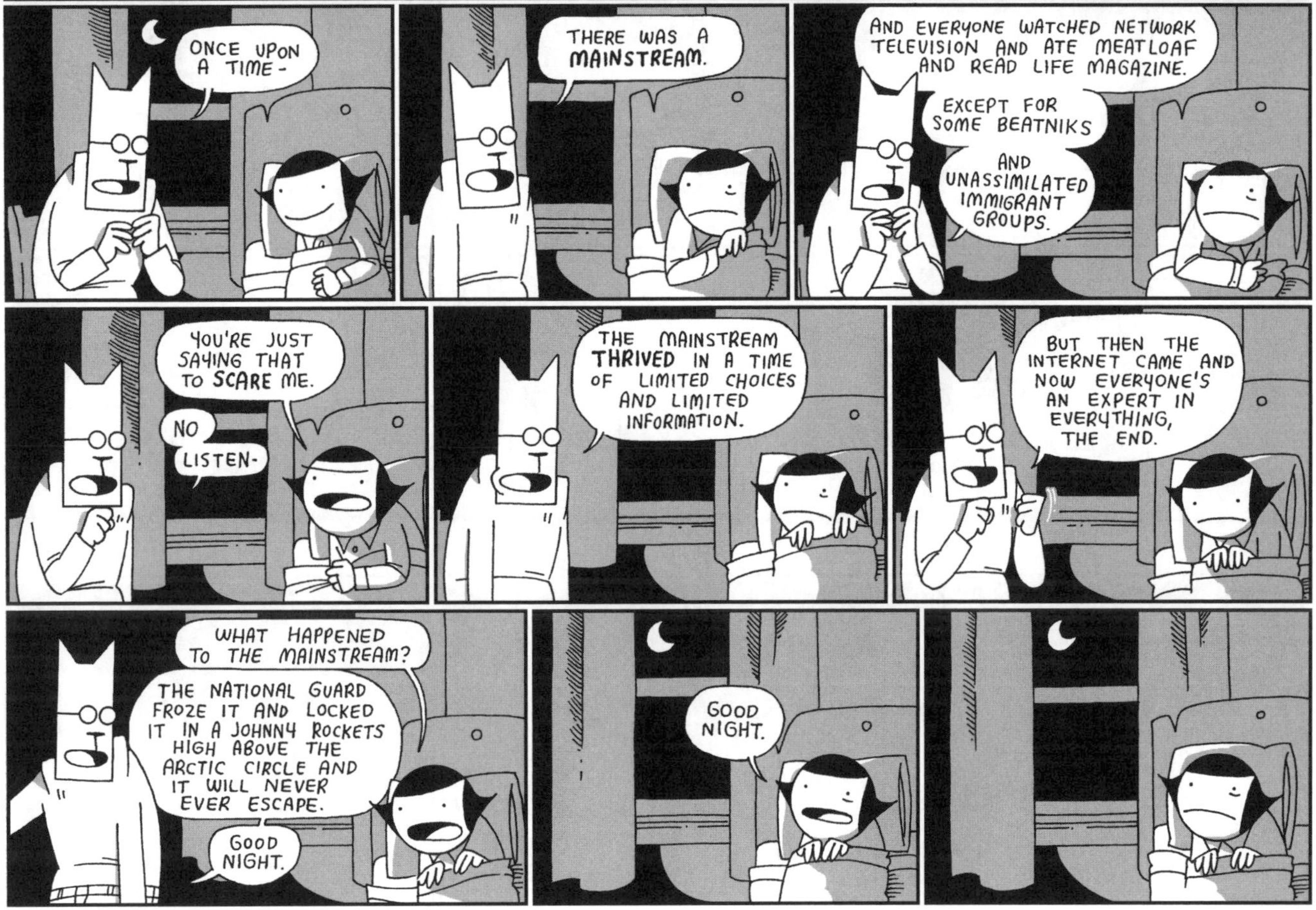

ONCE UPON A TIME-
THERE WAS A MAINSTREAM.
AND EVERYONE WATCHED NETWORK TELEVISION AND ATE MEATLOAF AND READ LIFE MAGAZINE.
EXCEPT FOR SOME BEATNIKS
AND UNASSIMILATED IMMIGRANT GROUPS.
YOU'RE JUST SAYING THAT TO SCARE ME.
NO
LISTEN-
THE MAINSTREAM THRIVED IN A TIME OF LIMITED CHOICES AND LIMITED INFORMATION.
BUT THEN THE INTERNET CAME AND NOW EVERYONE'S AN EXPERT IN EVERYTHING, THE END.
WHAT HAPPENED TO THE MAINSTREAM?
THE NATIONAL GUARD FROZE IT AND LOCKED IT IN A JOHNNY ROCKETS HIGH ABOVE THE ARCTIC CIRCLE AND IT WILL NEVER EVER ESCAPE.
GOOD NIGHT.
GOOD NIGHT.

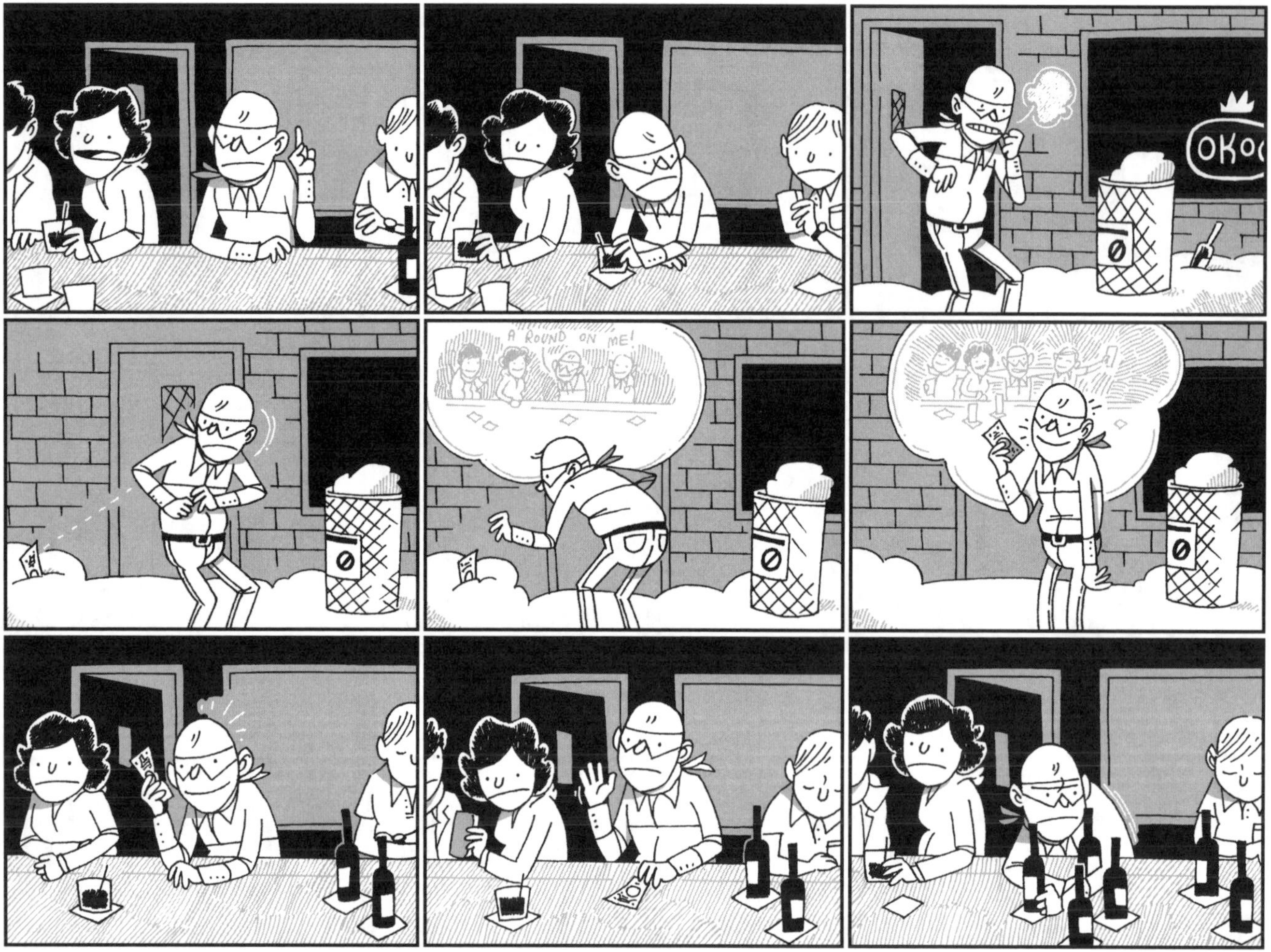
A ROUND ON ME!

The Banks of Denial

WHERE ARE THE CAPTAINS OF INDUSTRY WILLING TO GO DOWN WITH THE SHIP?
THE HAMBURGLERS OF CALAIS
FAT WITH PROFIT
BUT WILLING TO STEP UP WHEN CALLED UPON.
OUR CAPTAINS OF INDUSTRY DON'T MAKE ANYTHING BUT MONEY.
THE EMPLOYER MIGHT FEEL SOME RESPONSIBILITY TO THE EMPLOYEE
BUT THE SWINDLER HAS NO SYMPATHY FOR THE SWINDLED.
THAT'S NOT A SOCIETY
THAT'S A PYRAMID SCHEME!
IT DOES MAKE IT EASY TO FIND THE PHARAOHS RESPONSIBLE.

Brave Old World

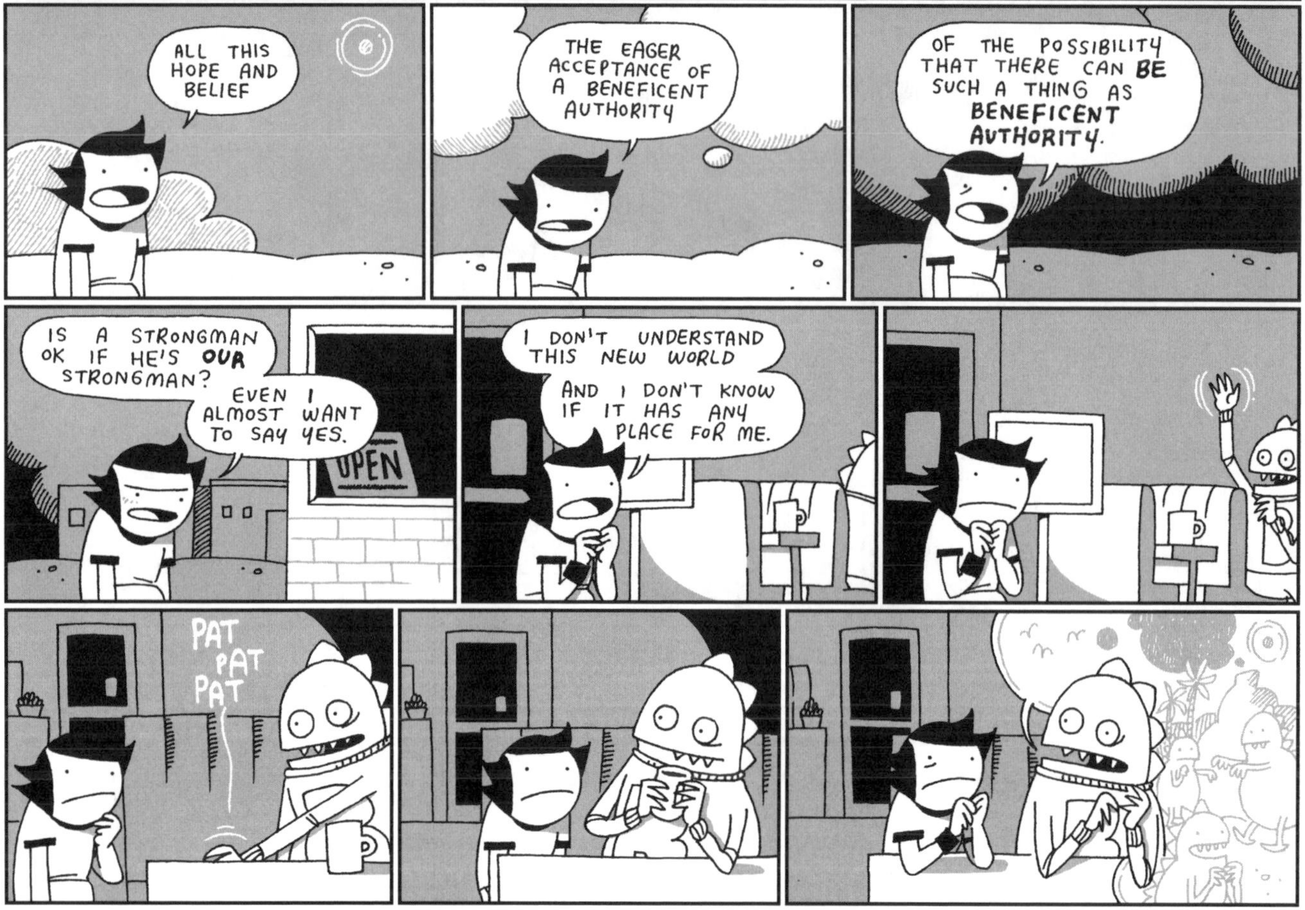
ALL THIS HOPE AND BELIEF
THE EAGER ACCEPTANCE OF A BENEFICENT AUTHORITY
OF THE POSSIBILITY THAT THERE CAN BE SUCH A THING AS BENEFICENT AUTHORITY.
IS A STRONGMAN OK IF HE'S OUR STRONGMAN?
EVEN I ALMOST WANT TO SAY YES.
OPEN
I DON'T UNDERSTAND THIS NEW WORLD
AND I DON'T KNOW IF IT HAS ANY PLACE FOR ME.
PAT PAT PAT

HEY!
DINOSAURS AREN'T EXTINCT.
THEY JUST BECAME BIRDS!
WINK

Chain of Command

WORK BIRTHDAYS.
CASUAL FRIDAYS.
LIKE WE'RE PRETENDING WORK IS SOME KIND OF NEGOTIATED AND CONSIDERED **CHOICE**
INSTEAD OF THE **PRICE** WE PAY FOR LIVING IN A SOCIETY WHERE ANYONE **BIGGER** OR **STRONGER** THAN US CAN'T JUST TAKE WHATEVER OF OURS THEY WANT.

Gang of Five

HURRY UP!
IT'S STARTING!
SEE THE OLD FACTORY IS BEING **HAUNTED** BY GHOSTS-
BUT WATCH OUT!
HERE COMES THE **VELVET UNDER-GROUND!**
THEY DRIVE AROUND IN A VAN AND SOLVE MYSTERIES.
THAT'S NOT THE VELVET UNDERGROUND.
RUN NICO
RUN!
I CAN'T WATCH.
THAT'S NOT NICO.
OH!
THE GHOSTS WEREN'T REAL!
THEY'RE JUST HELIUM-FILLED SILVER MYLAR BALLOONS.
YOU CAN'T TRICK US OLD MAN WARHOL!
THAT'S **NOT**-
OH.

When You Wish

WHAT DO YOU WANT?
UNDERPANTS.
GIFT CARDS TO DOLLAR GENERAL.
IT'S BETTER TO NOT BE DISAPPOINTED.
YOU **HAVE** TO BELIEVE IN THE IMPOSSIBLE!
EVERYTHING IN THE **WORLD** BELONGS TO PEOPLE WITH **MONEY** AND **POWER** AND **CONNECTIONS** AND **FAME**.
BUT THE IMPOSSIBLE IS **OURS**.
IT'S ALL WE'VE GOT!
DID YOU SEE THAT?
NOW WE OWE THE DISNEY CORPORATION TWELVE THOUSAND DOLLARS.

Guilty Pleasures

I LIKE VAMPIRE FICTION.
THE "VOWS" COLUMN?
IRONICALLY!
I LIKE DANCE POP IRONICALLY.
I LIKE CORN DOGS IRONICALLY.
I LIKE WINE COOLERS IRONICALLY.
AA AUGHHH!
IRONY ISN'T JUST SOME CHEAP WAY TO SAY YOU LIKE SOMETHING BUT ARE AFRAID TO ADMIT IT!
IRONY IS WHEN WORDS AND MEANING DIFFER!
I ENJOY SPENDING TIME WITH YOU.

Secret Handshakes

THE SELF-SELECTED CULTURAL ELITE USED TO BE A BIG DEAL.
OH YEAH!
BACK WHEN THERE WAS A "HIGH CULTURE"
I USED TO GO TO THEIR PARADE EVERY YEAR.
BUT NOW FOR EVERY VELVET UNDERGROUND
WHERE CRITICAL SUCCESS PRECEDES POPULARITY
THERE'S A MONKEES AND A JUDAS PRIEST AND A 2 LIVE CREW AND A KATY PERRY.
POPULARITY IS THE MARK OF FUTURE CRITICAL SUCCESS-
AND NOT THE OTHER WAY AROUND
LEAVING THE SELF-SELECTED CULTURAL ELITE ALWAYS TWENTY YEARS BEHIND EVERYONE ELSE.
JUST ANOTHER DYING SECRET SOCIETY WITH CONSPIRACY THEORIES ABOUT THE DOLLAR BILL AND FUNNY HATS.
THIS IS THE MEETING?
YEAH.
WHY BOTHER?
FREE PEANUTS.
MY LANDLORD TURNED OFF THE HEAT.

Hot Topic

OH MAN
OH MAN CHECK IT OUT
VAMPIRES ARE COOL.
VAMPIRES ARE COOL AGAIN
I KNEW THIS WOULD HAPPEN
I JUST HAD TO WAIT
OH MAN
VAMPIRES ARE COOL.
I'M GOING TO THE MALL!
I GUESS OLD VAMPIRES DON'T COUNT.

Pin the Tail

ARE WE PLAYING BLIND MAN'S BLUFF?
ARE WE PLAYING MARCO POLO?
IT'S A SURPRISE.
ARE WE PLAYING FIRING SQUAD?
COME ON.
I CAN'T SEE ANYTHING!
I DON'T KNOW HOW JUSTICE DOES IT.
I THINK SHE PEEKS.

Flushing Meadows-Corona Park

IT'S SOMETHING YOU'VE ALWAYS WANTED.
LOW-COST PREVENTATIVE HEALTH CARE?
REASONABLE LIMITS ON COPYRIGHT?
A HIGH-SPEED NATIONWIDE RAIL NETWORK?
A PING-PONG TABLE!
WHAT'S THAT?
THAT'S WHERE THE UMPIRE SITS.

Family Plan

WHAT DO YOU WANT FOR CHRISTMAS?
LEGITIMACY IN THE EYES OF SOCIETY.
A BLACKBERRY?
CLOSE ENOUGH.
VOWS OF AUSTERITY ARE FOR PEOPLE WHO BELIEVE IN THINGS.
I DON'T THINK I HAVE ENOUGH-
AND I'VE WASTED SO MUCH TIME.
BUT WE CAN MAKE OUR OWN!
IF MY LIFE'S GOING TO BE **MEANINGLESS** IT MIGHT AS WELL BE **COMFORTABLE**!
WE JUST NEED CUPS AND STRING.
IT'S NOT THE SAME.
HELLO?
HELLO?
I'M IN THE YARD.
I CAN ONLY TALK TO YOU.
WHO **ELSE** DO YOU CALL?

Scientific Method

THWACK
THWACK
THWACK
THWACK
SPLAT!
I TOLD YOU THOSE EGGS WERE BAD.
NOW LET'S TRY THE MILK!

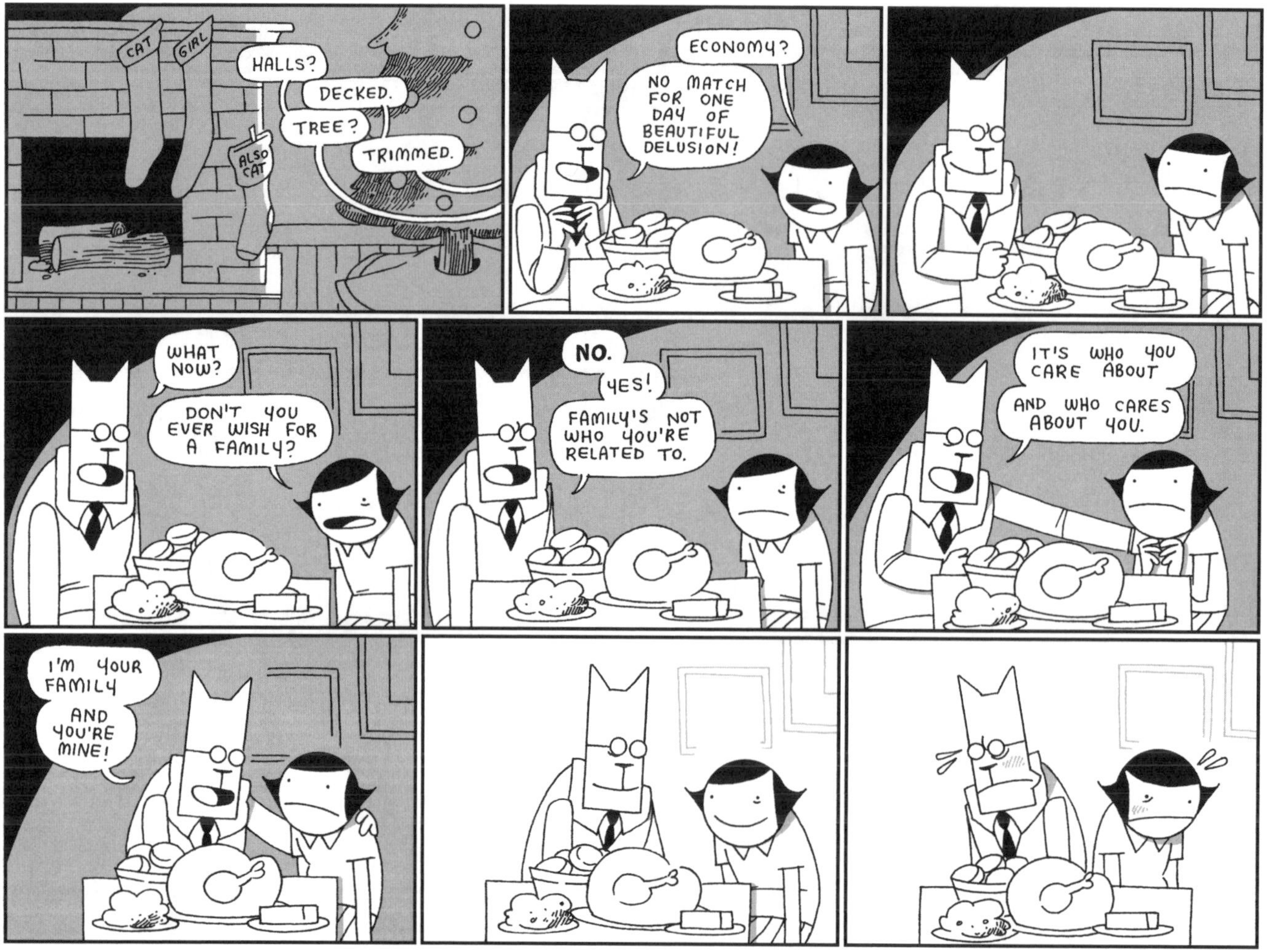

CAT
GIRL
ALSO CAT
HALLS?
DECKED.
TREE?
TRIMMED.
ECONOMY?
NO MATCH FOR ONE DAY OF BEAUTIFUL DELUSION!
WHAT NOW?
DON'T YOU EVER WISH FOR A FAMILY?
NO.
YES!
FAMILY'S NOT WHO YOU'RE RELATED TO.
IT'S WHO YOU CARE ABOUT
AND WHO CARES ABOUT YOU.
I'M YOUR FAMILY
AND YOU'RE MINE!

Untouchables

YOU KNOW WHAT'S THE MOST **DISGUSTING** THING IN THE WORLD?
A CRACKED EGGSHELL WITH A CLUMP OF HAIR INSIDE.
I-
I WAS GOING TO SAY WAR PROFITEERING BUT THAT TAKES IT.

In Time

WHAT ARE YOU DOING
SITTING HERE ALL BY YOURSELF
I WISH I WAS DEAD.
LONELY AS AN ITALIAN FEMINIST
NO
EVEN WHEN YOU'RE DEAD YOUR MEMORY LIVES ON IN THOSE WHO KNEW YOU.
I WISH I WAS DEAD AND EVERYONE WHO HAD EVER MET ME WAS DEAD TOO.
GRANTED!

Happy Together

DO YOU BELIEVE IN SERIAL MONOGAMY?
I LIKE CAPTAIN CRUNCH.
BUT NOT THAT MUCH.

Paging Doctor Godot

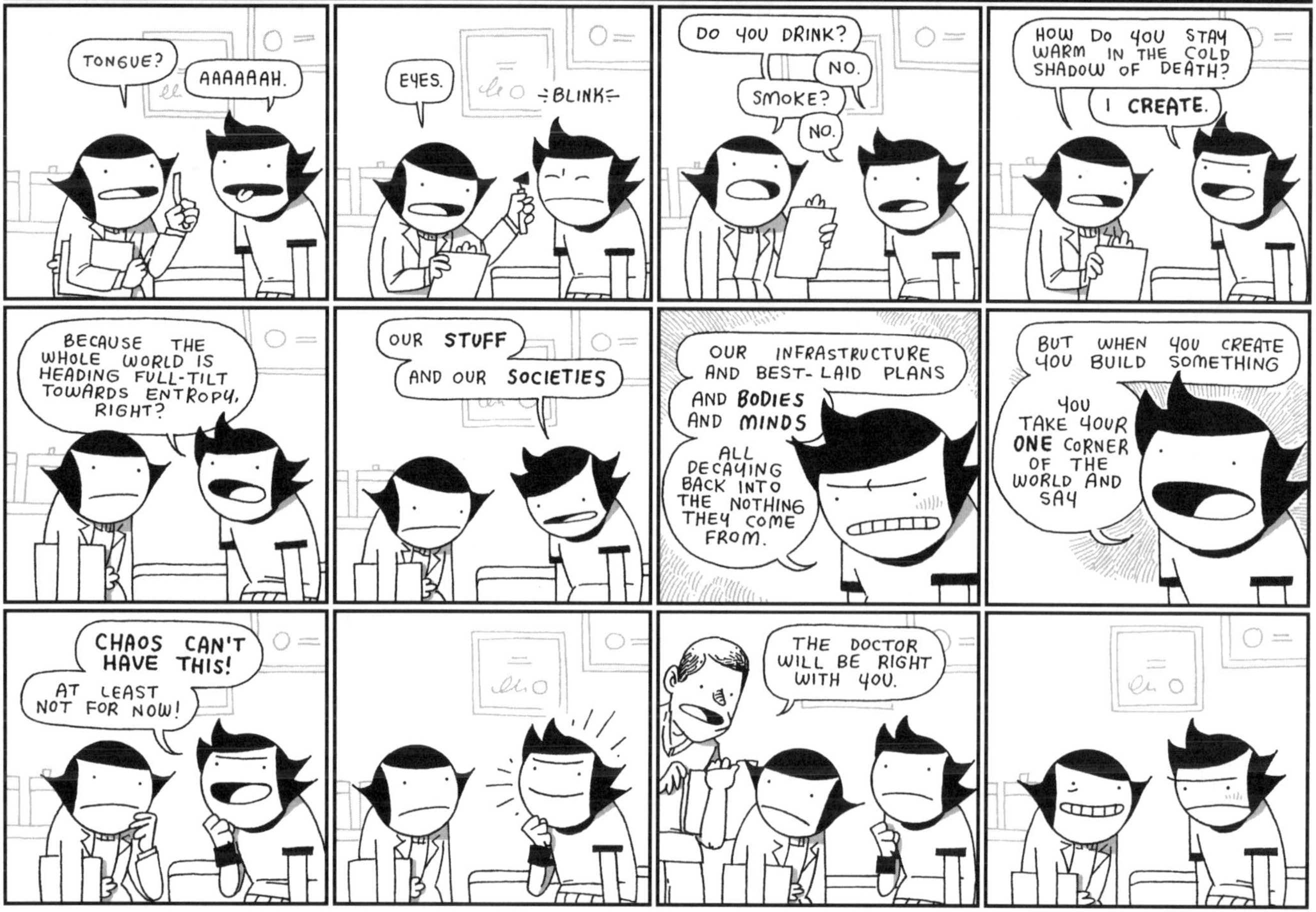

TONGUE?
AAAAAAH.
EYES.
BLINK
DO YOU DRINK?
NO.
SMOKE?
NO.
HOW DO YOU STAY WARM IN THE COLD SHADOW OF DEATH?
I CREATE.
BECAUSE THE WHOLE WORLD IS HEADING FULL-TILT TOWARDS ENTROPY, RIGHT?
OUR STUFF
AND OUR SOCIETIES
OUR INFRASTRUCTURE AND BEST-LAID PLANS
AND BODIES AND MINDS
ALL DECAYING BACK INTO THE NOTHING THEY COME FROM.
BUT WHEN YOU CREATE YOU BUILD SOMETHING
YOU TAKE YOUR ONE CORNER OF THE WORLD AND SAY
CHAOS CAN'T HAVE THIS!
AT LEAST NOT FOR NOW!
THE DOCTOR WILL BE RIGHT WITH YOU.

Table Service

HOW DO YOU STAY WARM IN THE COLD SHADOW OF DEATH?
DO YOU CREATE?
CREATE!
THE WORLD IS FULL OF STUFF.
AND LOOK AT ALL THE BOOKS ALREADY WRITTEN!
LOOK AT THE MOVIES ALREADY MADE!
AM I GOING TO MAKE SOMETHING BETTER THAN THAT?
OF COURSE NOT!
DO I CREATE.
NO!
I DO THE WORLD A FAVOR AND KEEP MY IDEAS TO MYSELF!
SO HOW DO YOU STAY WARM IN THE COLD SHADOW OF DEATH?
I COLLECT RECORDS.

Crossing Guard

STOP
PHWEET
DO YOU CREATE?
NO.
DO YOU COLLECT?
NO!
SO HOW DO YOU STAY WARM IN THE COLD SHADOW OF DEATH?
FIREWORKS.

The Size of it All

THE VAST PERFECT EMPTINESS OF SPACE.
WHAT CAN WE OFFER IT BUT OUR IMPERFECTION?
MAYBE I SHOULD LEARN TO KNIT.

SOMETIMES WHEN I VISIT A NEW PLACE
I PLAY THIS GAME
WHERE IF MORE PEOPLE ASK ME FOR DIRECTIONS THAN I ASK FOR DIRECTIONS
I WIN.
SOMETIMES I PLAY A GAME WHERE I DIVIDE THE COST OF EVERY ITEM I'M WEARING BY THE NUMBER OF TIMES I'VE WORN IT
AND IF IT ADDS UP TO UNDER TWO DOLLARS I WIN!
SOMETIMES I PLAY A GAME WHERE IF PEOPLE KNOW MORE ABOUT ME THAN I KNOW ABOUT THEM
I WIN.
DO YOU WIN A LOT?
THERE ARE SOME GAMES YOU LOSE JUST BY PLAYING.
SLOTS.
"I NEVER."
RUSSIAN ROULETTE.
HUNGRY, HUNGRY HIPPOS.
THEY'RE JUST PLASTIC HIPPOS!
MAYBE THE WAY YOU PLAY.

Currents

THINGS ARE GONNA TURN AROUND.
THINGS ARE GONNA TURN AROUND!
THINGS ARE GONNA TURN AROUND.
THINGS ARE GONNA TURN AROUND!
THINGS ARE GONNA TURN AROUND.
THINGS ARE GONNA TURN AROUND!
MAYBE JUST ENJOY THE RIDE.

Looks Good to Me

IS PERFECTION ATTAINABLE?
OR IS IT A UTOPIAN BYWORD FOR ALL THOSE THINGS WE DREAM OF BUT NEVER REACH?
WHO WANTS TO BE **PERFECT**?
LOOP SOME DRUMS IN GARAGEBAND
AUTO COLOR BALANCE YOUR PHOTOS
PERFECT!
PERFECT IS PROFESSIONAL
TRANSPARENT
INHUMAN.
PERFECT MEANS **GOOD** BUT IT'S NEVER MEANT **WORTHWHILE**.
PERFECT IS **EASY**
IMPERFECT IS THE NEW DESIRABLE!
WE LIVE IN A TIME OF RAGGED EDGES.
WELCOME OUR NEW AESTHETIC OVERLORDS!
NOT EVERYTHING NEEDS A POORLY SILKSCREENED DRAWING OF A BIRD ON IT.
IF YOU NEED ME I WILL BE LISTENING TO TAPE HISS IN MY ROOM.

A History of Cinema

AN AESTHETIC OF IMPERFECTION SHOWS THE HAND OF THE CREATOR IN THE FINISHED PRODUCT.
YEAH
LIKE LITERALLY
WHOOP
IN THE SHOT AGAIN.
INCOMPETENCE IS PART OF IT
SURE -
ED WOOD TRIED TO SUCCEED BY MAINSTREAM STANDARDS AND FAILED - BUT HE DEVELOPED AN INCOMPETENCE SO INDIVIDUAL THAT WE CELEBRATE IT TODAY.
AND AS MOVIES DEVELOPED OUTSIDE THE MAINSTREAM
INCOMPETENCE WAS RECOGNIZED AS ITS OWN CRAFT
SO THAT FLAT ACTING, STUNT CASTING AND EXPLOITATION -
USED PURPOSEFULLY AND AIMED TOWARDS AN UNDERGROUND AUDIENCE -
COULD MAKE THE CAREER OF JOHN WATERS.
AND TIME PASSED
AND AMATEUR MOVIES MET THE TECHNOLOGY TO LOOK MORE LIKE PROFESSIONAL MOVIES -
AND PROFESSIONAL MOVIES SOUGHT AUTHENTICITY BY LOOKING MORE LIKE AMATEUR MOVIES -
UNTIL AN AMATEUR MOVIE USED THE AUTHENTICITY OF INCOMPETENCE TO BECOME A MAINSTREAM SUCCESS -
THE BLAIR WITCH PROJECT.
THE BLAIR WITCH PROJECT?
NOTHING AGES FASTER THAN REALISM.

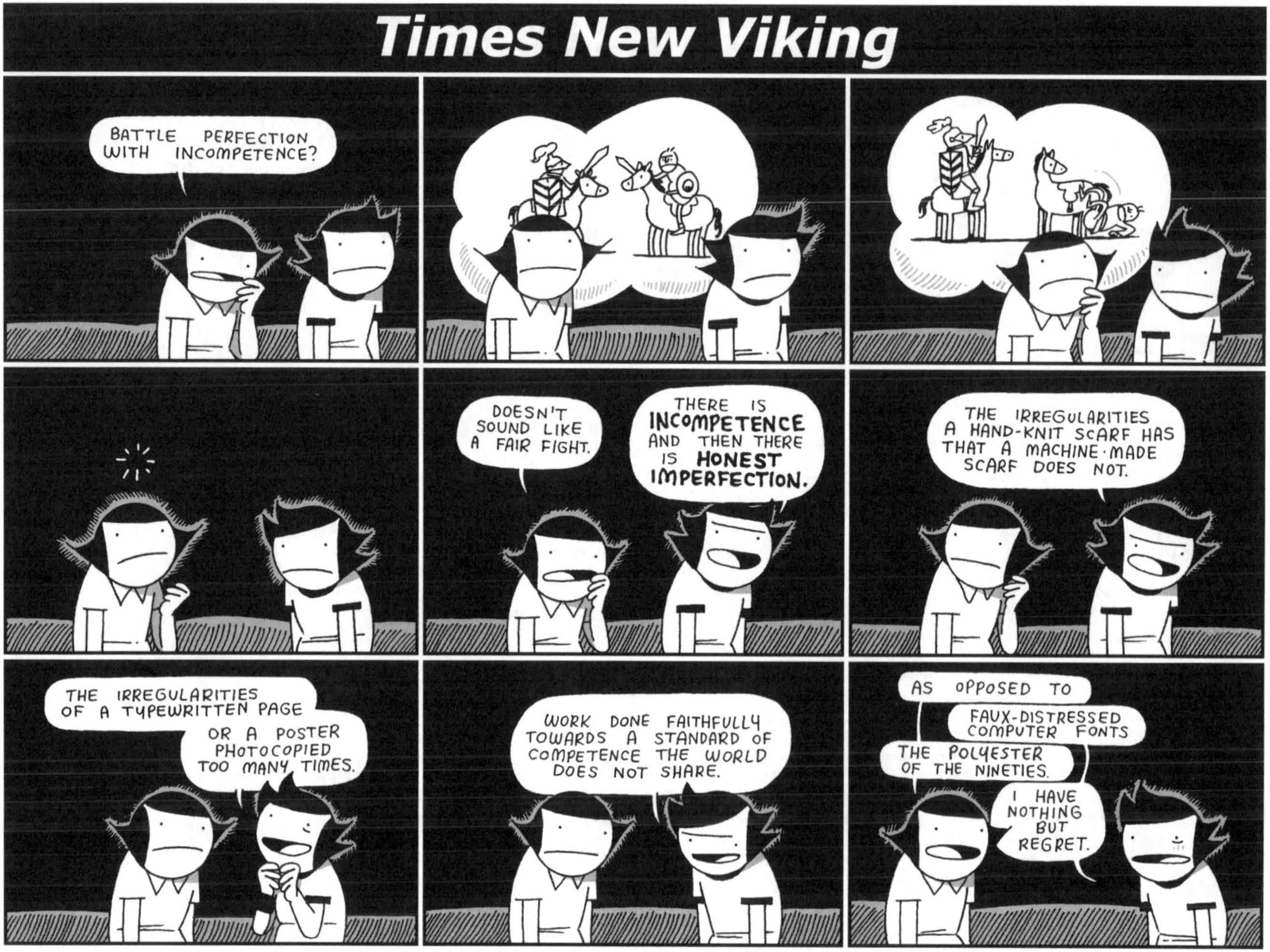

Times New Viking
BATTLE PERFECTION WITH INCOMPETENCE?
DOESN'T SOUND LIKE A FAIR FIGHT.
THERE IS INCOMPETENCE AND THEN THERE IS HONEST IMPERFECTION.
THE IRREGULARITIES A HAND-KNIT SCARF HAS THAT A MACHINE-MADE SCARF DOES NOT.
THE IRREGULARITIES OF A TYPEWRITTEN PAGE
OR A POSTER PHOTOCOPIED TOO MANY TIMES.
WORK DONE FAITHFULLY TOWARDS A STANDARD OF COMPETENCE THE WORLD DOES NOT SHARE.
AS OPPOSED TO
FAUX-DISTRESSED COMPUTER FONTS
THE POLYESTER OF THE NINETIES.
I HAVE NOTHING BUT REGRET.

BUT
BUT TYPEWRITTEN TEXT WAS A STANDARD OF MAINSTREAM PERFECTION ONCE
AS WAS LETTERPRESS-
DOT MATRIX-
HECK, CALLIGRAPHY-
ONLY WITH THEIR OBSOLESCENSE DID THEY BECOME IMPERFECT-
STYLISTIC QUIRKS FOR THOSE WISHING TO DISTANCE THEMSELVES FROM MAINSTREAM STANDARDS OF PERFECTION IN THE EASIEST WAY POSSIBLE!
SO?
WE SHOULD ALL FALL IN LINE BEHIND DIGITAL COMPETENCE?
WE WERE TALKING ABOUT PERFECTION.
THAT HAS NEVER BEEN A PROBLEM FOR ME.

All or Nothing

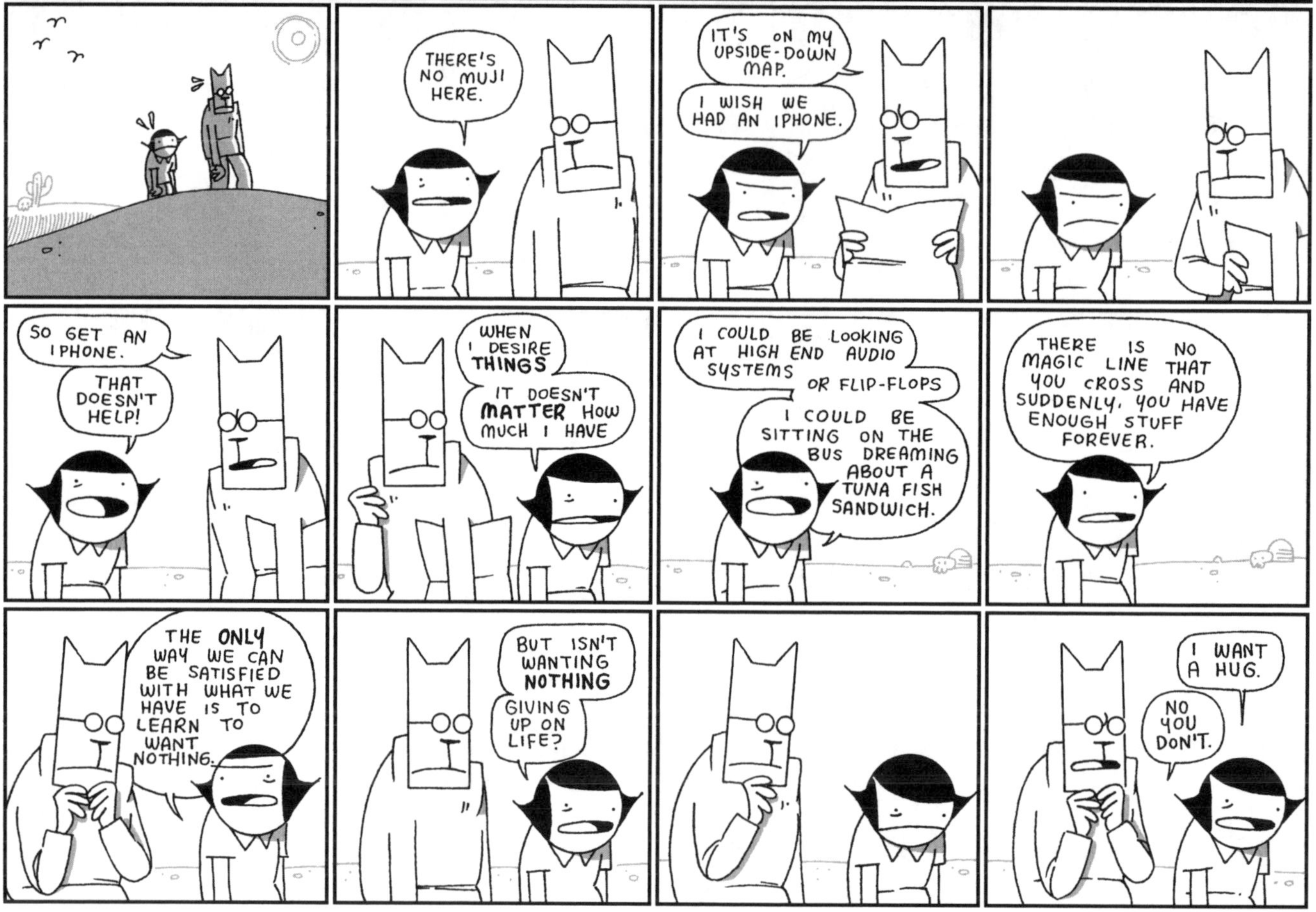

THERE'S NO MUJI HERE.
IT'S ON MY UPSIDE-DOWN MAP.
I WISH WE HAD AN IPHONE.
SO GET AN IPHONE.
THAT DOESN'T HELP!
WHEN I DESIRE THINGS
IT DOESN'T MATTER HOW MUCH I HAVE
I COULD BE LOOKING AT HIGH END AUDIO SYSTEMS
OR FLIP-FLOPS
I COULD BE SITTING ON THE BUS DREAMING ABOUT A TUNA FISH SANDWICH.
THERE IS NO MAGIC LINE THAT YOU CROSS AND SUDDENLY, YOU HAVE ENOUGH STUFF FOREVER.
THE ONLY WAY WE CAN BE SATISFIED WITH WHAT WE HAVE IS TO LEARN TO WANT NOTHING.
BUT ISN'T WANTING NOTHING
GIVING UP ON LIFE?
I WANT A HUG.
NO YOU DON'T.

ONE LEFT.
POP
POP
NO ONE LIKES TO TAKE THE LAST PIECE.
POP
IT'S SAD TO SEE SOMETHING MADE FINITE.
POP
POP
IT'S SAD TO SEE SOMETHING END.
IT'S COVERED IN GOOBER.
POP

WHERE'S THE PARTY AT?
WHERE'S THE PARTY AT?
WHERE'S THE PARTY AT?
WHERE'S THE PARTY AT?
WHERE'S THE PARTY AT?
WHERE'S THE PARTY AT?
WHERE'S THE PARTY AT?
WHERE ARE ALL THE SAD AND LONELY PEOPLE?
WOO!

WE'RE LOST.
I'LL CHECK GOOGLE MAPS.
AUGH
HERE WE ARE!
WHAT HAPPENED TO THE THRILL OF THE UNKNOWN?
LIGHT FALLING IN THE FOREST
BANJOS PLAYING
AND WHY AREN'T GAS STATION BATHROOMS AS FILTHY AS THEY USED TO BE?
A GAS STATION BATHROOM SHOULD BE A DARK CLOSET WITH TWO BUCKETS AND NO TOILET PAPER.
AND A SIGN ON THE BACK OF THE DOOR THAT SAYS "THIS IS WHAT YOU GET FOR LEAVING HOME."
JUST BECAUSE YOU PRIVILEGE THE WORLD OF YOUR CHILDHOOD DOESN'T MEAN EVERYONE ELSE HAS TO-
AND BESIDES-
YOU CAN BE NOSTALGIC FOR A CESSPOOL?
I CAN BE NOSTALGIC FOR MYSPACE.

WHAT DID PEOPLE DO BEFORE WIKIPEDIA?
-AND SNEEZY.
NOW THE SEVEN WONDERS OF THE ANCIENT WORLD.
HMM
THE PYRAMIDS AT GIZA.
THE COLOSSUS OF RHODES.
THE HANGING GARDENS OF BABYLON.
THE LIGHTHOUSE AT ALEXANDRIA-
IT'S ON THE TIP OF MY TONGUE, THE-
THE PANTHEON,
UH-
THE IKEA AT RED HOOK AND CARHENGE.
REALLY?
YEAH.
YOU'RE CERTAIN?
YEAH.
OH.
THE OSCILLOSCOPE IS OPEN.
LEND ME A PENCE FOR "TENNIS FOR TWO?"

♫HIT ME BABY ONE MORE TIME♫
SNAP
UGH
THOSE WERE THE DARK AGES-
WHEN INDIE BANDS WOULD COVER MAJOR POP SONGS
MAINTAINING THAT THEY WEREN'T BEING IRONIC
THEY JUST LIKED THE SONGWRITING-
AS IF THE SONGWRITING NEEDED THEM FOR LEGITIMACY.
HE WAS A SKATER BOY
SHE SAID SEE YA LATER BOY
I DON'T REMEMBER YOU COMPLAINING.
WE ARE ALL PRISONERS OF OUR ERA.

THWACK!
URRRGHH
I JUST REALIZED I DON'T CARE WHO WINS.
EVERYONE WANTS TO WIN!
WHAT IF I DIDN'T?
THEN YOU WIN TO GET WHAT EVERYONE ELSE WANTS- AND MAKE SURE THEY CAN'T HAVE IT!
WHAT IF I DIDN'T?
WHAT IF I JUST DIDN'T PLAY?
THWACK
YOU LOSE!

IF YOU'RE THE LITTLE FISH IN THE BIG POND
YOU KNOW YOU'RE INSIGNIFICANT
BUT YOU CAN TAKE SOLACE IN THE IMPORTANCE OF YOUR POND.
IF YOU'RE THE BIG FISH
IN THE LITTLE POND
WELL IF THE POND'S NOT IMPORTANT THE FISH HAS GOT TO START BELIEVING IN ITS OWN IMPORTANCE.
SO WHICH IS BETTER TO LIVE BY-
THE LIE OF THE SIGNIFICANCE OF THE FISH
OR THE LIE OF THE SIGNIFICANCE OF THE POND?
THE BIG POND'S GOT BETTER MUSEUMS.
BUT THE SUPERMARKETS ARE ALL TINY AND AWFUL.

CRYPTOZOOLOGY
THE SEARCH FOR CREATURES WRITTEN OFF AS FICTIONAL
FOR EXAMPLE
THE YETI.
BARK!
JUST BECAUSE NO ONE HAS SEEN THE YETI-
I HAVE!
YEAH?
WHERE?
THE LAUNDROMAT.
YETIS DON'T WEAR CLOTHES.
I NEVER SAID HE WAS DOING LAUNDRY!

MY BOOKS DESCRIBE THE YETI AS ELUSIVE.
HE'S GOT REASON TO BE.
THAT JERK OWES ME FORTY DOLLARS.
HE OWES **ME** SIXTY!
HE RAN INTO MY CAR AND DIDN'T LEAVE A NOTE!
HE OWES ME TWO HUNDRED!
HE OWES **ME** FIVE!
HE SLEPT ON MY COUCH FOR A **MONTH** AND DIDN'T HELP WITH A **SINGLE** UTILITY BILL!
I GAVE HIM TEN BUCKS FOR PIZZA AND HE PRETENDED THERE WASN'T ANY CHANGE!

IF THIS LIFE IS ALL WE'VE GOT
WHAT'S THE ARGUMENT AGAINST HEDONISM?
EXCEPT THAT IT SEEMS KIND OF TAWDRY.
SO **SOCIETY** IS OUR ARGUMENT AGAINST HEDONISM.
DUH!
AND THE MORE YOU HAVE **INVESTED** IN SOCIETY THE EASIER HEDONISM IS TO **PUT OFF** -
ID AND SUPEREGO!
FREUD SAID IT.
HIS THEORIES HAVE ALL THE WEIGHT OF A JOKE ON A POPSICLE STICK.
SO GO ENJOY YOUR HEDONISM THEN!
IT JUST DOESN'T SOUND LIKE MUCH FUN.

WE CAN GO BOWLING.
NO.
HIKING?
NO-
KARAOKE!
THAT'S NOT REALLY MY THING.
THE RODEO.
NOT MY THING.
ROLLERSKATING.
NOT MY THING.
THE **ROLLER SKATING RODEO.**
IT'S JUST NOT MY THING.
WHAT **IS** YOUR THING?
MAYBE I DON'T HAVE ONE.

MAP
MAP
MAP
MAP
MAP
HOW DO YOU GET TO RIKERS ISLAND?
PRACTICE PRACTICE PRACTICE!

WHAT'S THE ANSWER?
CHIPS AND SALSA!
WHAT?
CHIPS AND SALSA!
WHAT **CAN'T** BE IMPROVED BY CHIPS AND SALSA? THE **ANSWER** IS **ALWAYS** CHIPS AND SALSA!
HOW DID YOU DO ON THE GRE?
CHIPS AND **SALSA**.

PHONE
CAMERA
MUSIC PLAYER
COMPUTER
EVERYTHING NO ONE REALLY NEEDS IN JUST ONE DEVICE!
SURE IS CONVENIENT-
IF YOU'VE GOT THE MONEY.
YOU'RE JEALOUS!
I DON'T WANT ANY MORE THAN WHAT EVERYONE ELSE HAS GOT.
SINCE WHEN IS IT A HUMAN RIGHT TO LISTEN TO MUSIC EVERYWHERE YOU GO?
TO CAPTURE EVERY INSIGNIFICANT MOMENT
TO COMMUNICATE
EVERYTHING
EVERYWHERE
WHAT'S MORE HUMAN THAN COMMUNICATION?
ENVY.
GREED.
SELF-PITY.
INCOMPETENCE.
AGRICULTURE.
SANDWICHES.

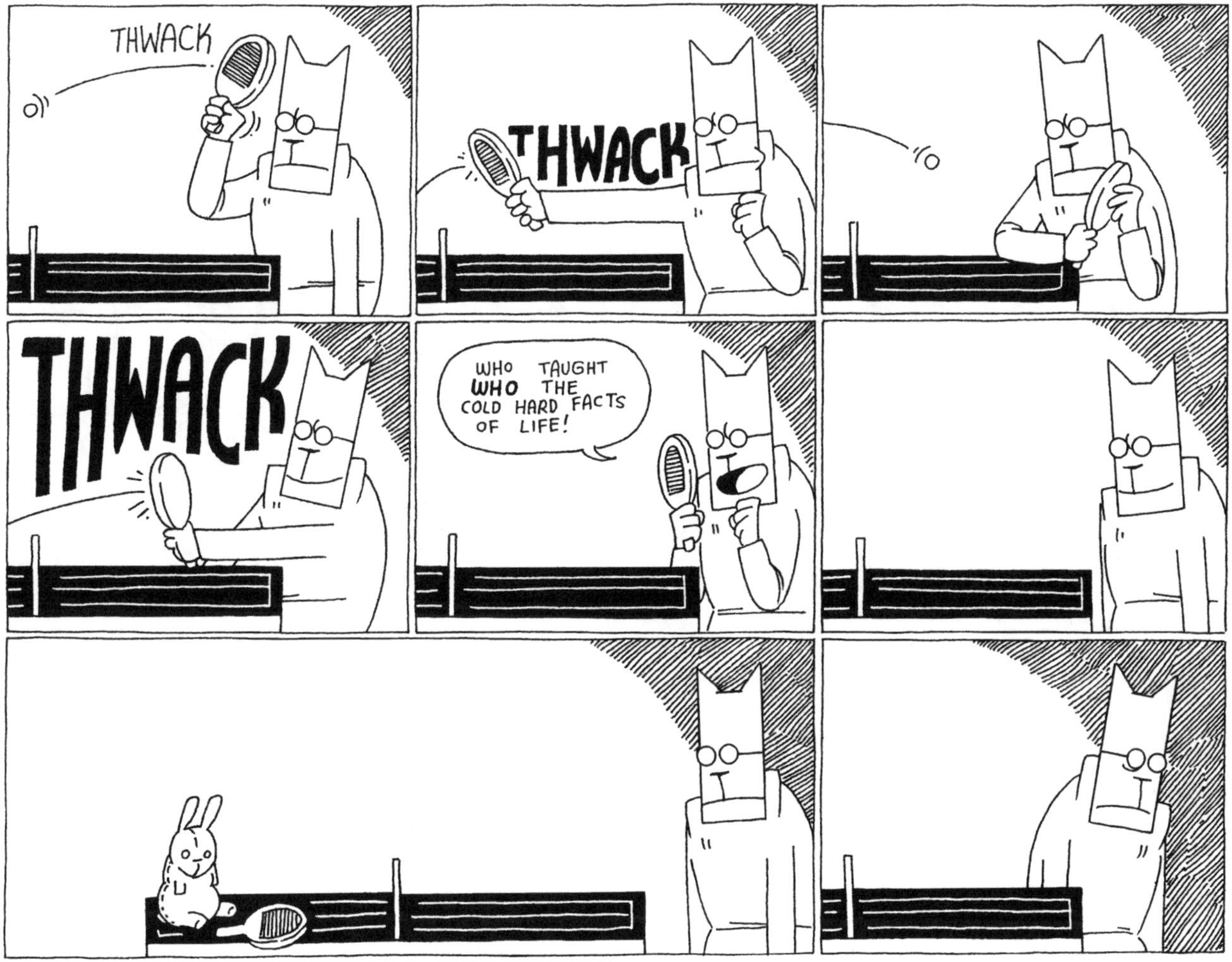
THWACK
THWACK
THWACK
WHO TAUGHT WHO THE COLD HARD FACTS OF LIFE!

WHY DID WE GET ALL THIS STUFF?
IT MADE US HAPPY
I ENVY THE NOMAD.
FOR A LITTLE WHILE
YOU GET YOUR TENT-
YOUR SPICES-
YOUR GREAT LOVE OF POETRY-
AND THEN IT JUST MADE US SADDER.
AND YOU ARE GOOD TO GO!
BUT
IT'S NOT LIKE WE'RE TIED TO THE LAND THROUGH AGRICULTURE-
OR COMMUNITY-
OR A SENSE OF PLACE-
WE'RE A MOBILE SOCIETY!
AND AS OUR MOBILITY INCREASES- SO DOES OUR CRUSHING COMMITMENT
TO STUFF.
WELL-
I AM A NOMAD
AND I PRIZE MY MOBILITY ABOVE ALL THINGS!
GOOD RIDDANCE!
IT'S A NEW DAY!
BURN THEM WHERE WE STAND!
THAT'S MY COMPUTER.
WE CAN'T GET RID OF SCAMPERS!

DEATH BEFORE DISHONOR.
DISHONOR FIRST,
THEN DEATH.
WAIT
WAIT
WAIT
WAIT
WAIT
WAIT
DISHONOR-
DEATH-
AND THEN I'LL PICK UP A PIZZA.
PIZZA FIRST!
I'M STARVING.

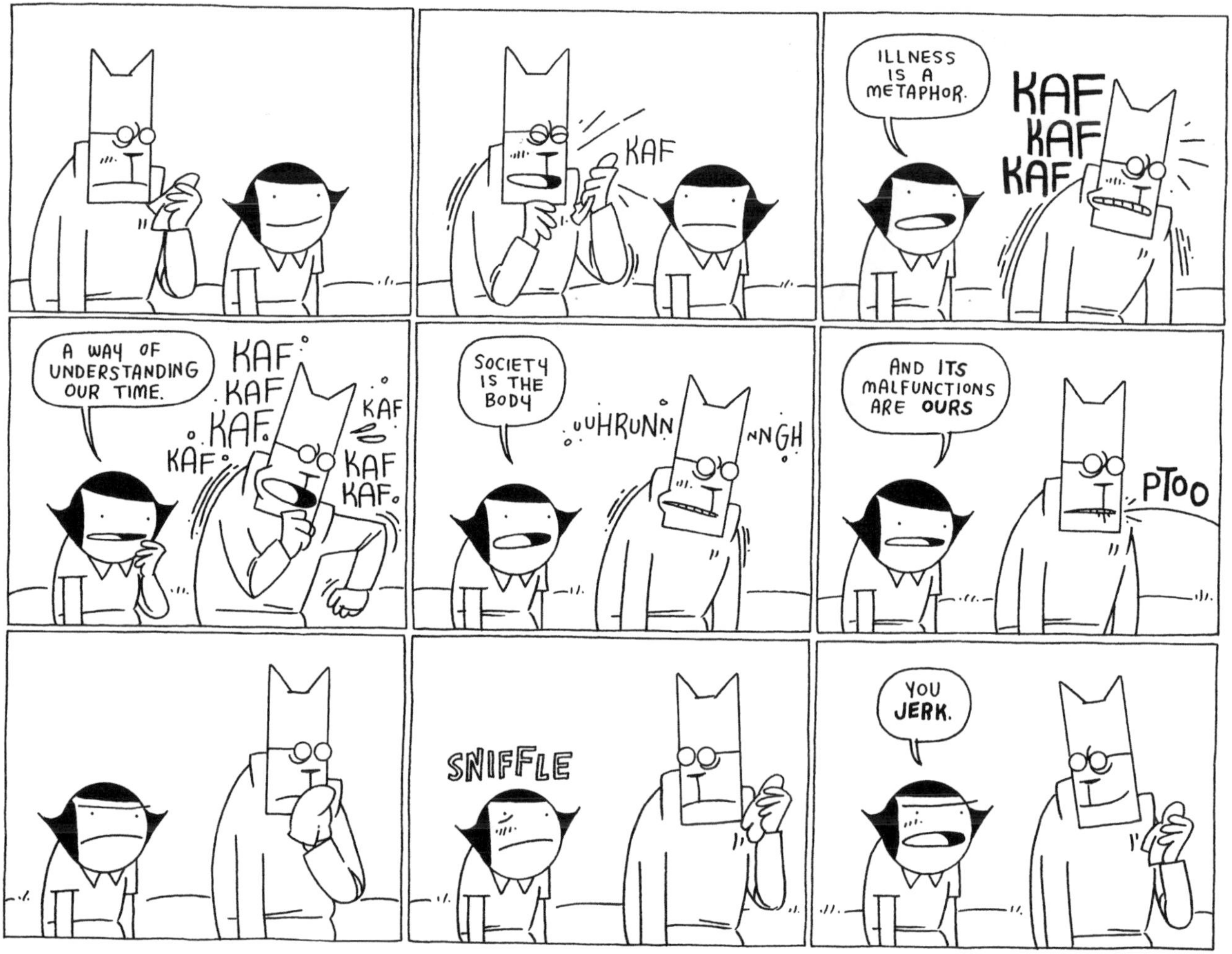
KAF
ILLNESS IS A METAPHOR.
KAF KAF KAF
A WAY OF UNDERSTANDING OUR TIME.
KAF KAF KAF KAF
KAF KAF KAF
SOCIETY IS THE BODY
UUHRUNN
NNGH
AND ITS MALFUNCTIONS ARE OURS
PTOO
SNIFFLE
YOU JERK.

The Flatulent Ghost

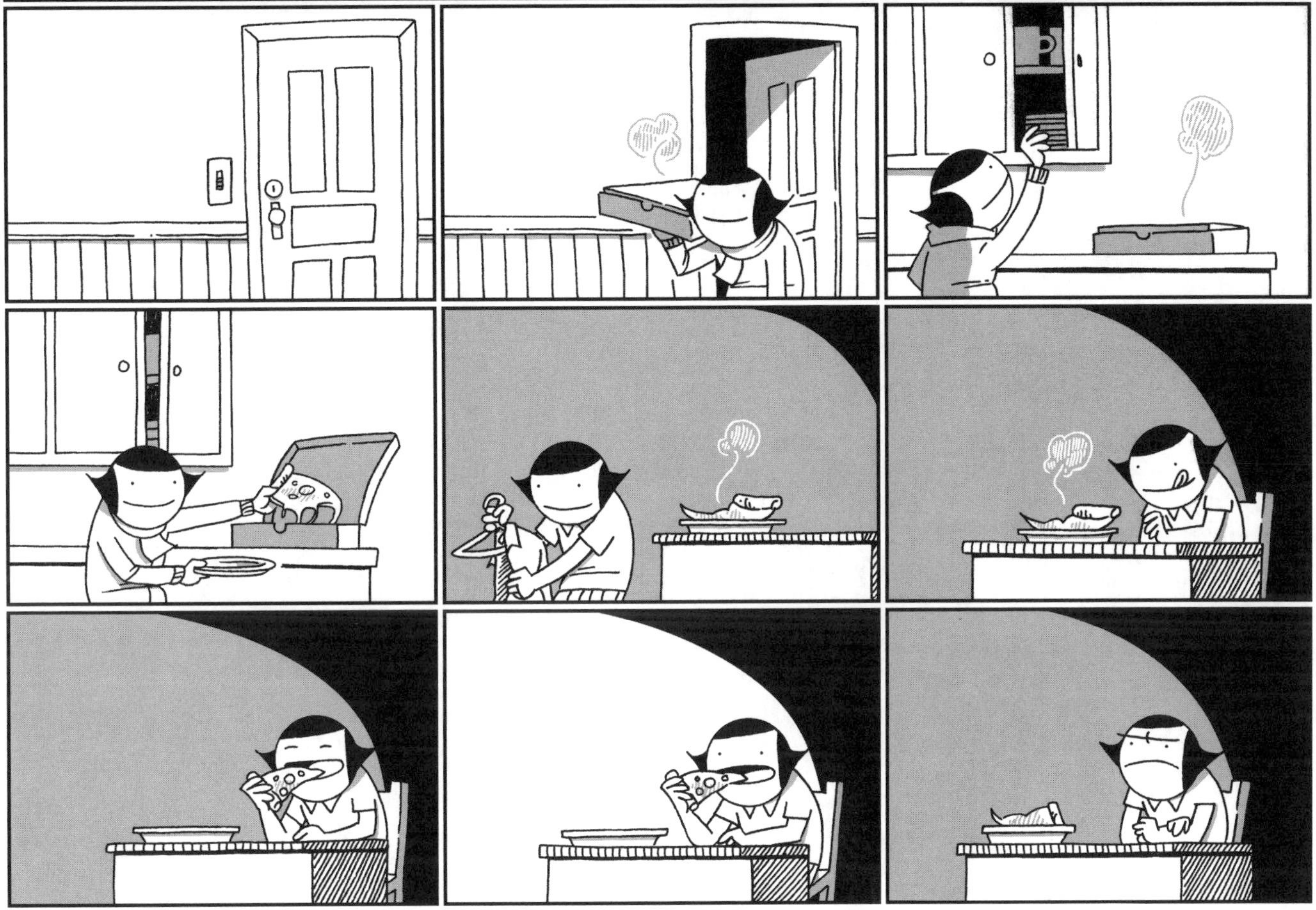

Boogiemen

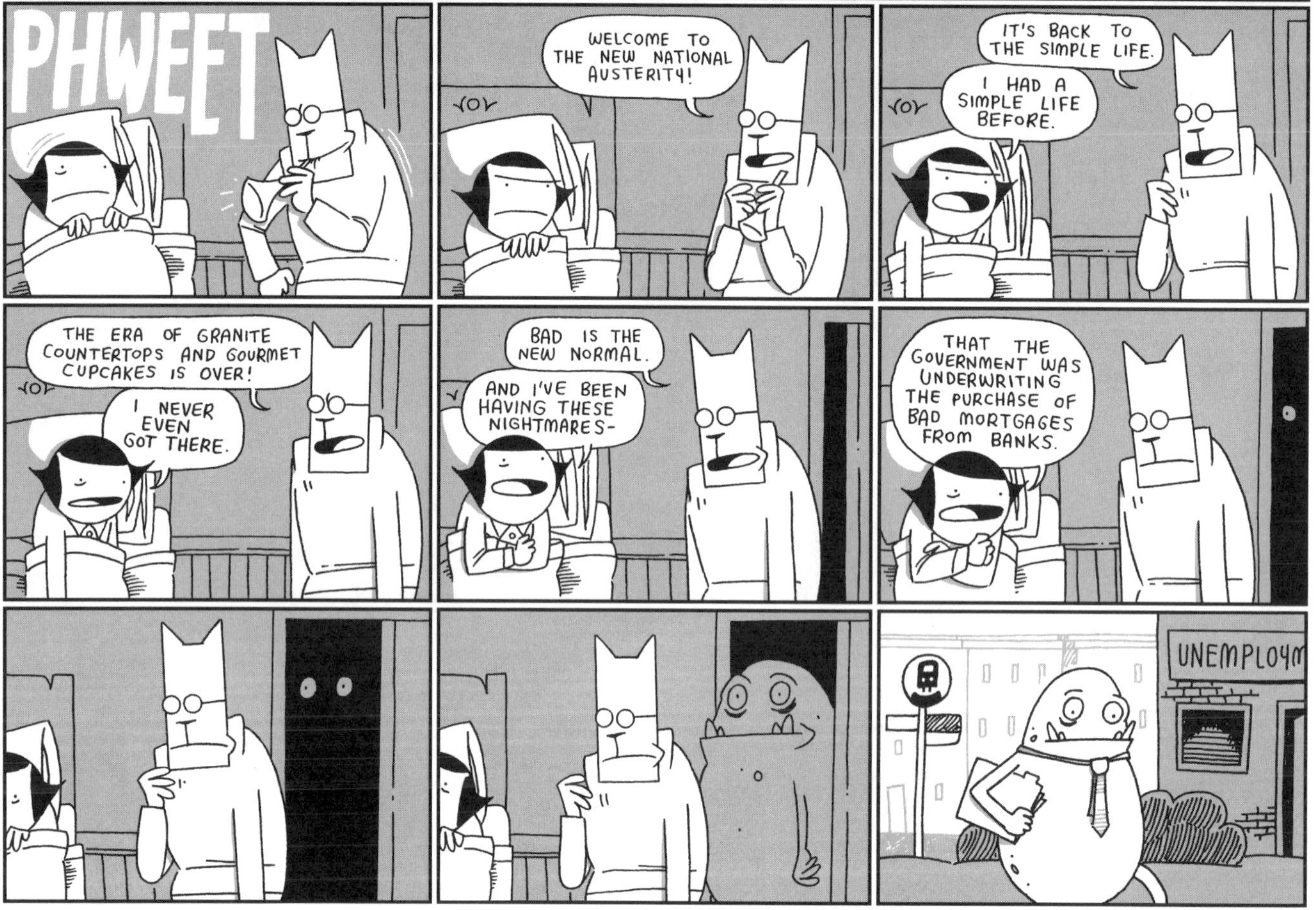
PHWEET
WELCOME TO THE NEW NATIONAL AUSTERITY!
IT'S BACK TO THE SIMPLE LIFE.
I HAD A SIMPLE LIFE BEFORE.
THE ERA OF GRANITE COUNTERTOPS AND GOURMET CUPCAKES IS OVER!
I NEVER EVEN GOT THERE.
BAD IS THE NEW NORMAL.
AND I'VE BEEN HAVING THESE NIGHTMARES-
THAT THE GOVERNMENT WAS UNDERWRITING THE PURCHASE OF BAD MORTGAGES FROM BANKS.
UNEMPLOYM

Eight Track Wonders of the Ancient World

I'M GOING TO MAKE WHAT I WANT TO MAKE
AND WHO CARES WHAT PEOPLE THINK.
BUT
CREATION IS COMMUNICATION
NOT A COMPROMISE-FREE STATEMENT OF EGO.
THE GREAT PYRAMID?
METAL MACHINE MUSIC?
IF THOSE AREN'T COMPROMISE-FREE STATEMENTS OF EGO WHAT ARE THEY?
NOTHING IS CREATED OUTSIDE OF CONTEXT
AND CONTEXT SHIFTS CONSTANTLY
GRAND MEANINGS CRUMBLE BRICK BY BRICK
UNTIL THEY DON'T LOOK LIKE WHAT THEY DID
IF THEY LOOK LIKE ANYTHING AT ALL.
IF YOU AREN'T CREATING TO COMMUNICATE
WHAT'S THE POINT?

Qualifications

DO YOU HAVE A COPY OF YOUR RESUME?
HOW FAST CAN YOU TYPE?
EEEEEEEEEEEE

Tania
WE'LL CAN OUR OWN PRESERVES!
PRESERVE OUR OWN MEAT!
CATCH OUR OWN BOTULISM.
HELLO 2005!
EVERYONE'S RAISING CHICKENS NOW.
BACK TO WALMART THEN.
DOES EVERYONE HAVE TO BUY SO MUCH JUST TO SIMPLIFY THEIR LIFE?
YES?
THAT'S KIND OF THE POINT.
PEOPLE DON'T WANT WHAT THEY SAY THEY WANT.
THEN HOW DOES ANYONE KNOW WHAT ANYONE IS TALKING ABOUT?
WORDS ARE THE HOSTAGES OF THEIR SPEAKERS
AND THEIR MEANINGS ARE HELD CAPTIVE IN A WAREHOUSE BY THE OCEAN.
UNTIL THOSE MEANINGS...
...INEVITABLY...
COME AROUND TO OUR WAY OF THINKING.
AND THEN THE WORDS WILL HAVE TO MEAN WHAT WE TELL THEM TO MEAN.

War Games

SOME PEOPLE BECOME HOSTAGES OF THEIR WORDS.
THEIR WORDS TURN AGAINST THEM?
OR THE WORDS OF OTHERS-
OR THE MEANING TURNS AGAINST THEM.
THAT DOUBLE-CROSSER!
AND THE MEANING ESCAPES-
AND THE WORDS FALL IN LINE.
-WHILE YOU WEREN'T LOOKING-
SUDDENLY YOU'RE OUTNUMBERED.
-AND NOW MEANING IS LOOKING FOR REVENGE.
HAS ANYONE SEEN MEANING LATELY?
EVER?

The Search for Meaning

Escape of the Flatulent Ghost

Everything Is Somewhere

WHERE DID ALL THE MEANING GO?
WHAT STINKS IN HERE?

Things That Go Bump in the Night

YOU LOOKED WHERE?
THE CLOSET AT THE BOTTOM OF THE STAIRS.
YOU OPENED THE BASEMENT CLOSET?
WE WERE LOOKING FOR MEANING!
I TOLD YOU TO NEVER GO IN THERE!
YOU SAY THAT ABOUT THE BATHROOM TOO.
YOU'VE OPENED PANDORA'S BOX
AND NOW THE WINGED SPECTERS OF OUR OWN FRAILTIES WILL BLANKET THE EARTH.
THE AIR SO THICK WITH MEANING IT SUFFOCATES YOU
ALL THE TROUBLES OF MANKIND -
FREE AT LAST.
WHY WERE THEY IN THE BASEMENT?
I HAD COMPANY!

Regrets

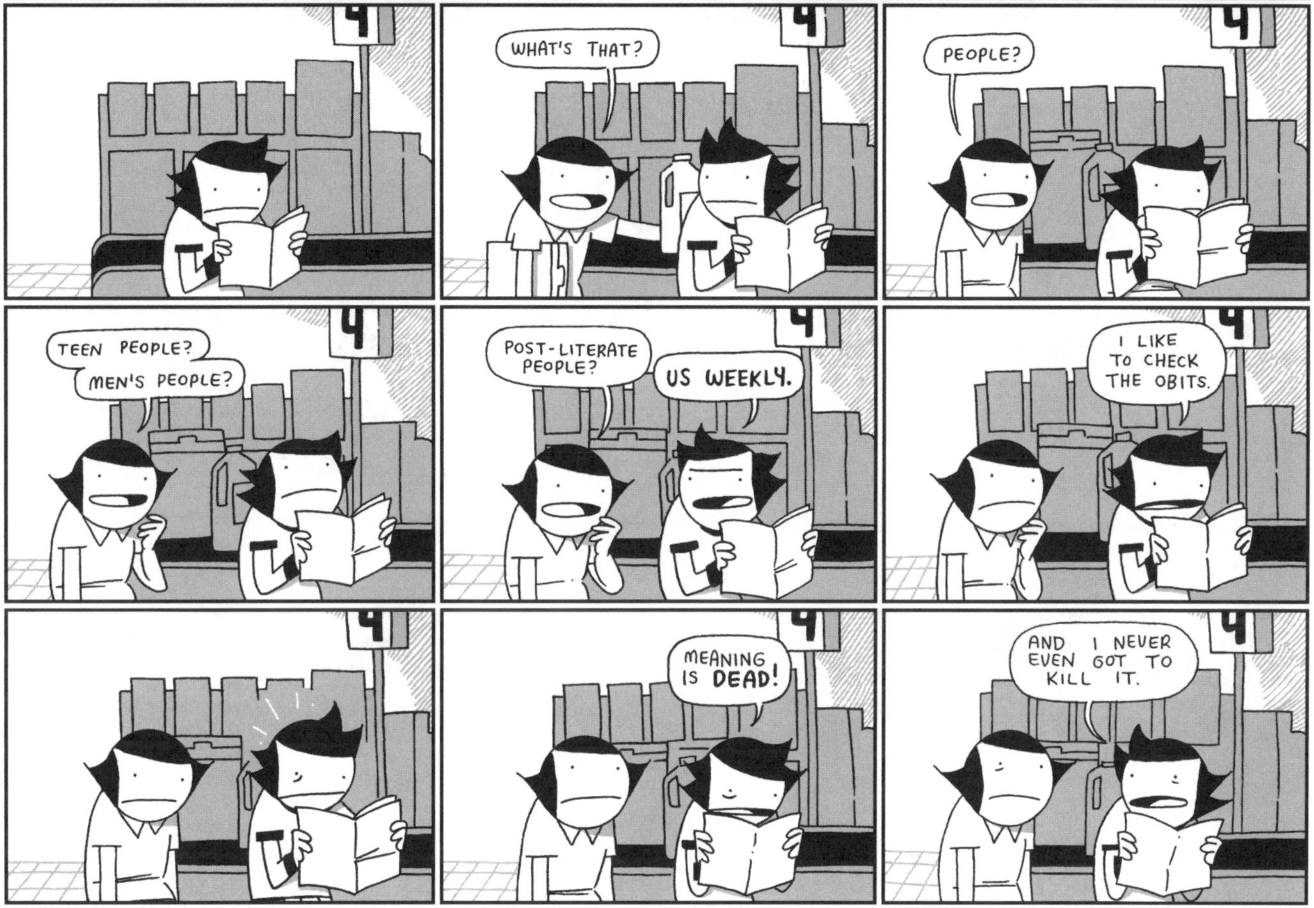
WHAT'S THAT?
PEOPLE?
TEEN PEOPLE?
MEN'S PEOPLE?
POST-LITERATE PEOPLE?
US WEEKLY.
I LIKE TO CHECK THE OBITS.
MEANING IS DEAD!
AND I NEVER EVEN GOT TO KILL IT.

The Rise and Fall of Steve Reich

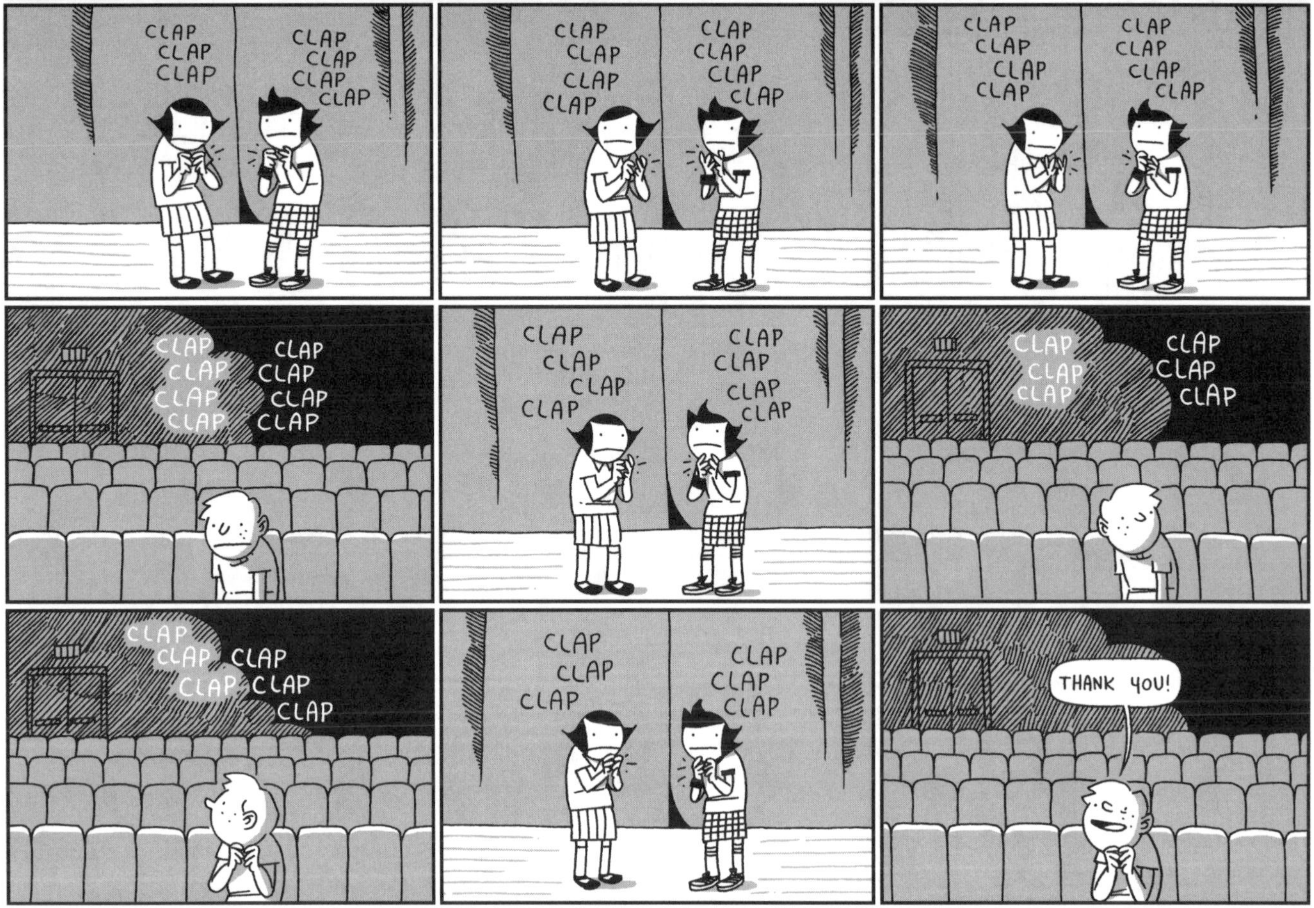
CLAP CLAP CLAP
CLAP CLAP CLAP CLAP
CLAP CLAP CLAP CLAP
CLAP CLAP CLAP CLAP
CLAP CLAP CLAP CLAP
CLAP CLAP CLAP CLAP
CLAP CLAP CLAP CLAP
CLAP CLAP CLAP CLAP
CLAP CLAP CLAP CLAP
CLAP CLAP CLAP CLAP
CLAP CLAP CLAP
CLAP CLAP CLAP
CLAP CLAP CLAP
CLAP CLAP CLAP
CLAP CLAP CLAP
CLAP CLAP CLAP
THANK YOU!

Political Action Committee

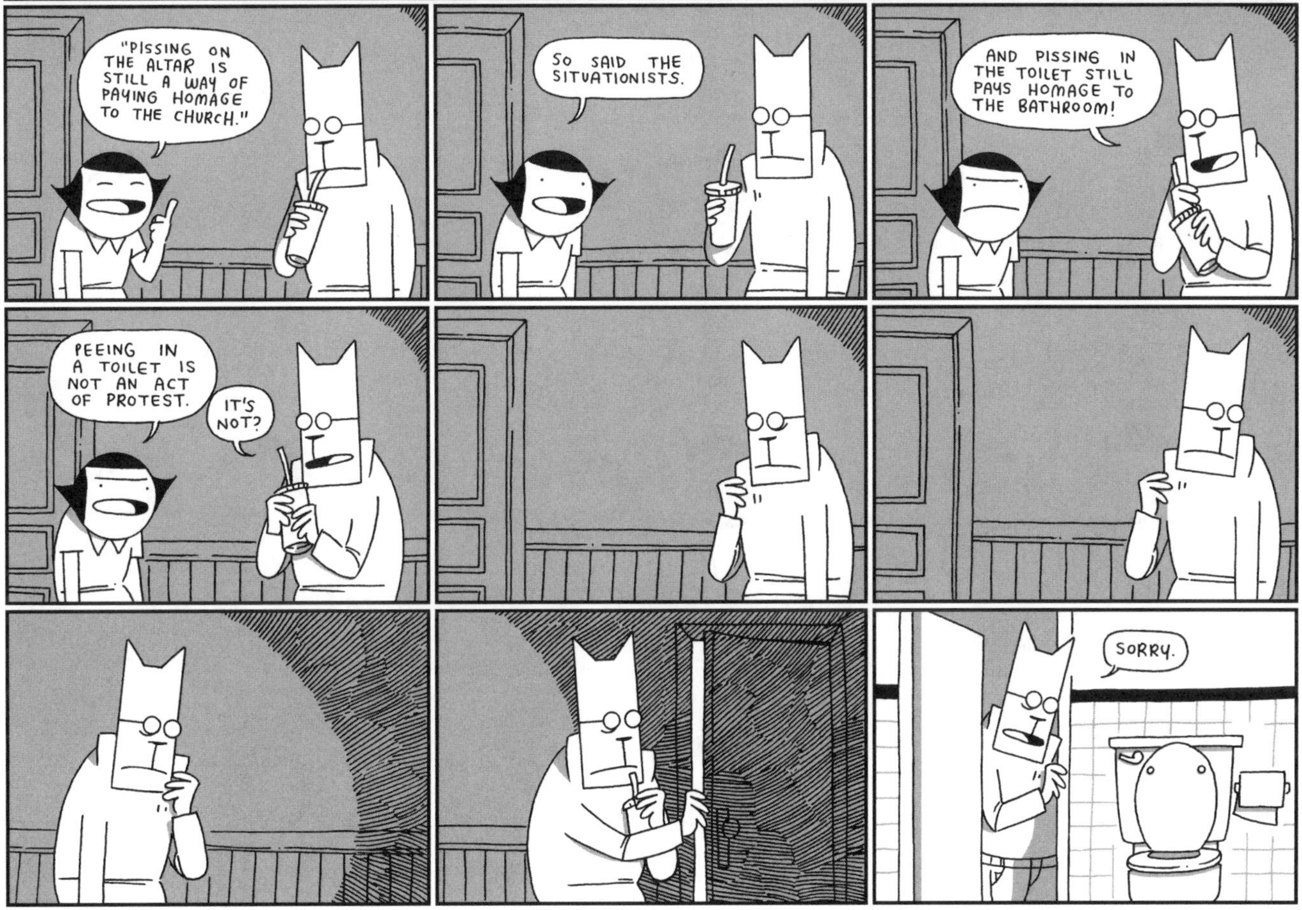

"PISSING ON THE ALTAR IS STILL A WAY OF PAYING HOMAGE TO THE CHURCH."
SO SAID THE SITUATIONISTS.
AND PISSING IN THE TOILET STILL PAYS HOMAGE TO THE BATHROOM!
PEEING IN A TOILET IS NOT AN ACT OF PROTEST.
IT'S NOT?
SORRY.

Evangelists

FINALLY!
PEOPLE ARE WILLING TO TALK OPENLY ABOUT ATHEISM.
THE WIND IS AT OUR BACKS!
FINALLY
PEOPLE WHO DON'T BELIEVE IN GOD CAN BE JUST AS OBNOXIOUS AS PEOPLE WHO DO.
WE HAVE OUR OWN MEETINGS NOW.
WE HAVE OUR OWN CHARITIES!
WE HAVE OUR OWN JONAS BROTHERS.
ATHEISM'S GONE MAINSTREAM.
THERE IS NO GOD.

The Loneliness of the Long Distance Writer

AUGH!
I QUIT!
DON'T QUIT!
ALL THE BEAUTIFUL DREAMS ARE IMPOSSIBLE.
WHAT MATTERS IS THAT WE CHASE THEM.
AND SOMETIMES WHAT WE THINK IS A BEAUTIFUL DREAM IS A BEAR.

Everyone Is the Prisoner of Themselves

NO ONE UNDERSTANDS ME.
THANK GOD!

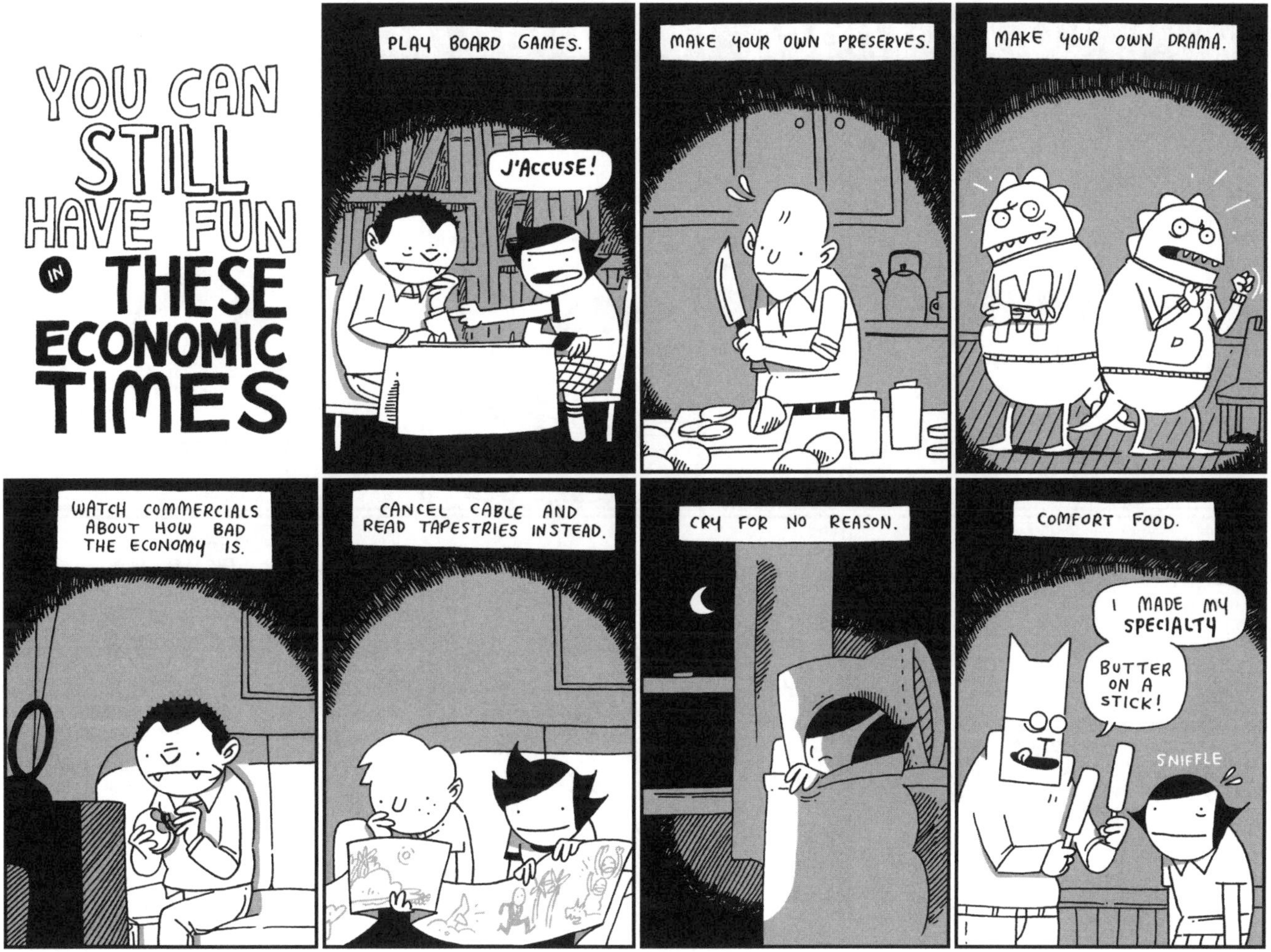
YOU CAN STILL HAVE FUN IN THESE ECONOMIC TIMES
PLAY BOARD GAMES.
J'ACCUSE!
MAKE YOUR OWN PRESERVES.
MAKE YOUR OWN DRAMA.
WATCH COMMERCIALS ABOUT HOW BAD THE ECONOMY IS.
CANCEL CABLE AND READ TAPESTRIES INSTEAD.
CRY FOR NO REASON.
COMFORT FOOD.
I MADE MY SPECIALTY
BUTTER ON A STICK!
SNIFFLE

In These Troubled Times

TELL ME A JOKE?
THE NEW YORK TIMES TUESDAY STYLE SECTION.
ONE I HAVEN'T HEARD BEFORE!

Little Boxers Made of Ticky Tack

YOU FIGHT?
YOU SHOULD SEE ME-
BAP BAP BAP
TAKING ON A MATADOR-
THE SPANISH GUYS WITH THE HATS AND THE CAPES.
NO NO
THE THING THAT MEANS ANOTHER THING.
YOU FIGHT METAPHORS.
APATHY!
MEDIOCRITY!
MORTALITY!
DO YOU WIN?
I STEP INTO THE RING
SIT IN AN UNCOMFORTABLE CHAIR FOR A FEW HOURS
EAT A BOWL OF CEREAL FOR DINNER
AND THEN FALL OVER.
YOU NEED GLOVES FOR THAT?
I BITE MY NAILS SOMETHING AWFUL NOW.

Up and Down

EVER SINCE THE "STOCK MARKET" CRASHED-
$
$
AND THE BANJO-PLAYING BEARS SET OUT FOR CALIFORNIA
LOOKING FOR FARM WORK
IT'S BEEN TOUGH.
BUT PEOPLE WANT GOOD TIMES EVEN IN BAD TIMES
RIGHT?
SO HUSTLE ON OVER TO THE BAD TIMES AMUSEMENT PARK!
$
BAD TIMES

BANK STATEMENT
WE'VE GOT A HAUNTED HOUSE-
AAAAAAA
CONCESSIONS-
BUTTER ON A STICK
NEW! FRIED BUTTER ON A STICK
GAMES AND PRIZES FOR KIDS
WIN a MORTGAGE
AND ALL KINDS OF RIDES!
THE MUSIC INDUSTRY
CLOSED
TRY THE MOVIE INDUSTRY
INCLUDING OUR BRAND NEW NUMBER ONE ATTRACTION
THE SELF-PITY SHIP!
SELFPITY
SELFPITY
WHISH
WHISH
SELFPITY
NO ONE REALLY LOVES ME!
WOO!

Castaway

"HOW DO I GET INTO THE NEW YORKER?"

Cause and Affect

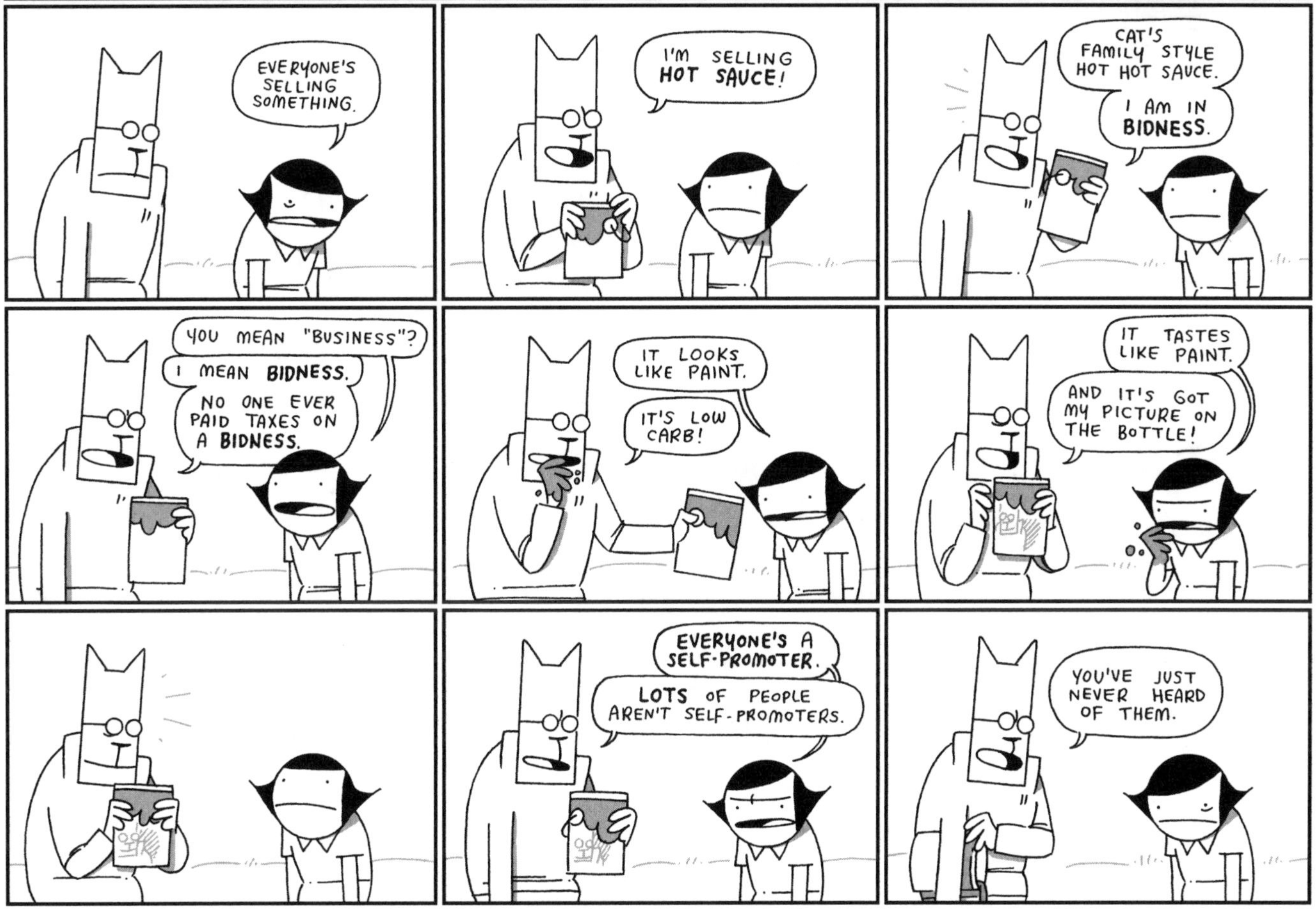
EVERYONE'S SELLING SOMETHING.
I'M SELLING HOT SAUCE!
CAT'S FAMILY STYLE HOT HOT SAUCE.
I AM IN BIDNESS.
YOU MEAN "BUSINESS"?
I MEAN BIDNESS.
NO ONE EVER PAID TAXES ON A BIDNESS.
IT LOOKS LIKE PAINT.
IT'S LOW CARB!
IT TASTES LIKE PAINT.
AND IT'S GOT MY PICTURE ON THE BOTTLE!
EVERYONE'S A SELF-PROMOTER.
LOTS OF PEOPLE AREN'T SELF-PROMOTERS.
YOU'VE JUST NEVER HEARD OF THEM.

One-Upsmanshippers

I LIKED GEORGE SAUNDERS BEFORE YOU LIKED GEORGE SAUNDERS.
I SAW "BRANDED TO KILL" FIRST.
I STOPPED LISTENING TO M.I.A. BEFORE YOU STOPPED LISTENING TO M.I.A.
I'VE ONLY STARTED LISTENING TO CLAP YOUR HANDS SAY YEAH RECENTLY.
I LIKED SRIRACHA FIRST.
I LIKED TAPATIO.
I WAS VEGAN BEFORE YOU WERE VEGAN.
AND I GAVE UP ON IT FIRST!
I LIKED "X" BEFORE YOU LIKED "X" -
OF COURSE I LIKED X!
WHO DOESN'T LIKE X?
I WAS DISGUSTED BY THE CORRUPT VENALITY OF POP CULTURE BEFORE YOU WERE.
AND I EMBRACED THE CORRUPT VENALITY OF POP CULTURE AS A VIBRANT COUNTERPOINT TO THE OUT OF TOUCH EUROCENTRIC PREENINGS OF SELF-PROCLAIMED HIGH CULTURE!
FIRST!
I APPROPRIATED THE EIGHT BIT AESTHETIC FOR CRAFTY KNITWARE BEFORE YOU DID.
I'M THE LOST DAUPHIN!

A Rising Tide Lifts All Boats

WE DON'T **HAVE** A BOAT!

Choices Choices

THE WORLD HAS ENOUGH ART AND LITERATURE FOR A THOUSAND LIFETIMES.
MY MINOR CONTRIBUTIONS ONLY DILUTE THE POWER OF WHAT ALREADY EXISTS.
I AM THROUGH WITH CREATING.
YESSSS.
NO!
I'M THROUGH WITH DESTRUCTION TOO-
WE OUGHT TO HOLD ON TO THE THINGS THAT WE HAVE-
BESIDES-
CREATION AND DESTRUCTION WERE NEVER OPPOSITES-
NOT WHEN THEY'RE THE SAME THING.
THE SAME THING!
WITHOUT DESTRUCTION THERE IS NO CREATION- JUST ASK A REAL ESTATE AGENT.
BUILDY BUILDY TAKES TWICE AS LONG AS SMASHY SMASHY!

THE OPPOSITE OF CREATION AND DESTRUCTION
IS STASIS.
IS STASIS THE ONLY OPTION WE HAVE LEFT?

Dolor General

RUSTLE RUSTLE
DIET SODA.
IT'S A METAPHOR!
WE WANT THE FIZZY SWEETNESS BUT NOT THE CALORIES.
CALORIES IS THE POINT OF FOOD.
WE WANT MOMENTARY PLEASURE SHORN FROM CONSEQUENCE.
IMAGINE A DIET SODA CULTURE
CHEAP CREDIT
EASY DEBT
THE PURSUIT OF LUXURY
A CONCEPT OF LUXURY WITH NO RELATIONSHIP TO QUALITY
AND THE COUNTERFEIT INDUSTRY THAT SUCH "LUXURY" DESERVES.
OUR PERSONAL GRASPING CULPABILITY IN THE BINGE AND PURGE ECONOMY-
DIET SODA.
COOKIES?
I LIKE COOKIES.

Tall Tales

AND WHEN SHE OPENED HER EYES
AND LOOKED IN THE MIRROR-
-THE FACE THAT LOOKED BACK AT HER-
WAS THE FACE OF A HIPSTER!
AAAAAAA
AAAAAAAAAH!
PFF
HIPSTERS ARE JUST OUR DECADE'S VERSION OF SATANIC CHILD-ABUSE RITUALS-
POP CULTURE NEEDS THEM SO IT INVENTS THEM-
-BUT HIPSTERS AREN'T REAL.
SURE THEY ARE!
I'VE SEEN THEIR BIKE LANES!
WHAT IF THEY HEAR US?
EVERYONE'S SEEN A HIPSTER BUT NOBODY IS ONE.
THEY'RE BOOGIEMEN!
SPOOKY STAND-INS FOR WHAT WE REALLY FEAR AND DESPISE!
HIPSTERS DON'T EXIST!
WHOSE IDEA WAS IT TO GO CAMPING IN PORTLAND?

Invaders

MIDDLE-CLASS SUBURBIA IS AS REAL AS ANYWHERE-
BUT IT'S NOT ALLOWED THE PRIVILEGE OF AUTHENTICITY.
AUTHENTICITY IS A PRIVILEGE.
AND ALSO- THE OPPOSITE OF PRIVILEGE.
NEXT YOU'LL TELL ME A HOT DOG IS A SAUSAGE.
THE "REAL" WORLD IS A CRUEL ONE.
A COLD HUNGRY STRUGGLE IS "REAL"
"AUTHENTIC"
BOREDOM IN COMFORT IS NOT.
SO THE CHILDREN OF MIDDLE-CLASS SUBURBIA-
DENIED THE AUTHENTICITY OF THEIR OWN LIVES-
SEEK OUT AND CLAIM THE AUTHENTICITY OF OTHERS.
IT'S CULTURE AS THAT OLD MOVIE TRICK-
KNOCK SOMEONE OUT

DRESS IN THEIR CLOTHES
AND INTEGRATE INTO THEIR SOCIETY.
WHAT IF A LOT OF PEOPLE WANT TO GET INSIDE
AND EVERYONE WHO LIVES THERE GETS KNOCKED OUT
AND EVERYONE WALKING AROUND
IS IN STOLEN CLOTHES?
YES!

Return of the Moon-Men of Mars

EARTH PEOPLE!
AH!
DAMMIT.
IT HAS BEEN YEARS SINCE OUR LAST VISIT TO EARTH
AND YOU HAVE MANAGED TO FREE NEITHER MUMIA NOR TIBET.
I WOULD LIKE TO OWN ONE SHIRT WITHOUT MUSTARD ON IT.
HOW HAVE YOU BEEN?
UH-HEY.
HEY!
HEY GUYS.
SAME OLD SAME OLD.
YOU CAN'T GO ANYWHERE WITHOUT RUNNING INTO SOMEBODY.
AND THAT'S WHY WE DON'T WEAR SWEATPANTS OUTSIDE!

Cat and Girl versus Contemporary Art

WHAT DO YOU THINK IT MEANS?
IT'S A GUESSING GAME.
LIKE GUESSING HOW MANY JELLY BEANS ARE IN A JAR-
IT'S A LITTLE SKILL AND A LOT OF LUCK EVEN WHEN THE GAME ISN'T RIGGED.
BUT IF I DO GUESS THE RIGHT NUMBER OF JELLY BEANS
I MIGHT WIN A TURKEY DINNER.
WHAT CAN I WIN FOR GUESSING THE MEANING OF ART?
A MOTORBOAT.
REALLY?

Anniversaries

SORRY.
DOG

True Believers

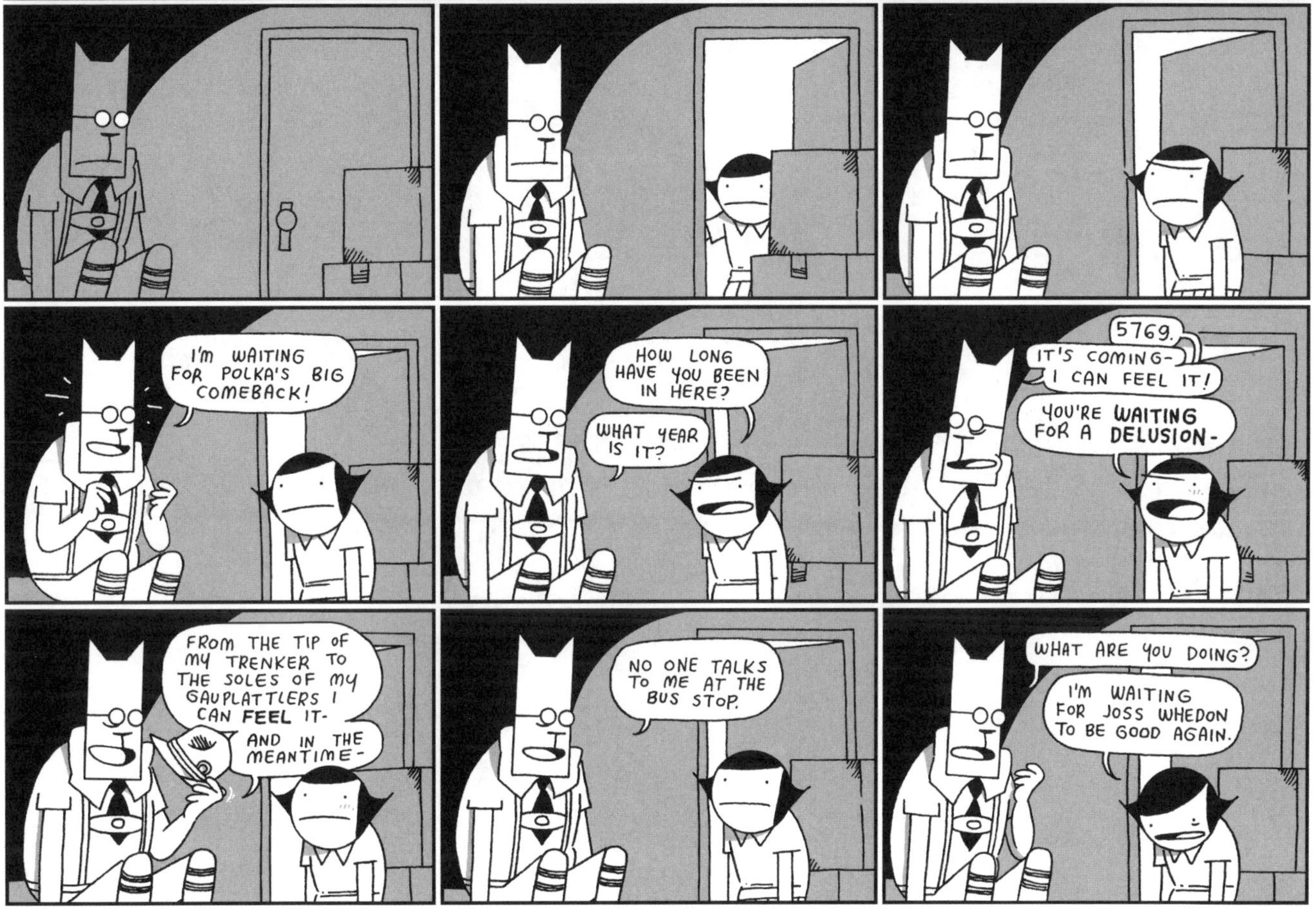
I'M WAITING FOR POLKA'S BIG COMEBACK!
HOW LONG HAVE YOU BEEN IN HERE?
WHAT YEAR IS IT?
5769.
IT'S COMING-
I CAN FEEL IT!
YOU'RE WAITING FOR A DELUSION-
FROM THE TIP OF MY TRENKER TO THE SOLES OF MY GAUPLATTLERS I CAN FEEL IT-
AND IN THE MEANTIME-
NO ONE TALKS TO ME AT THE BUS STOP.
WHAT ARE YOU DOING?
I'M WAITING FOR JOSS WHEDON TO BE GOOD AGAIN.

History Will Vindicate Cat and Girl

I QUIT.
NO!
IF HARRY TRUMAN QUIT WHEN THINGS GOT TOUGH
HE NEVER WOULD HAVE BEEN PRESIDENT.
IF THE FLAMING LIPS QUIT WHEN THINGS GOT TOUGH
THEY NEVER WOULD HAVE MADE MUSIC THAT PEOPLE ACTUALLY LIKE.
IF HENRY DARGER QUIT AFTER A FEW YEARS
NO ONE WOULD DEFEND THAT CRAZY PEDOPHILE!
THERE ARE PEOPLE WHO ARE GOOD AT STUFF AND THEN
THERE ARE THE PEOPLE WHO JUST STICK AROUND LONG ENOUGH.

Cat and Girl Follow Up

YOU OWE ME AN ARCH DELUXE.
CRAZY
I WENT WITH CRAZY

PO
OF
CLUNK
I COME FROM THE FUTURE
I CAME FROM AN OPEN HOUSE.
THOSE CONDOS?
IRON FIXTURES
IRON APPLIANCES
LIKE BRONZE ISN'T GOOD ENOUGH ANY MORE.
THIS WAS SUPPOSED TO BE A MASTODON RUN.
IT'S REALLY CHANGED SINCE THEY BUILT THE TARGET.

Basic Cable

"THE GOOD FIGHT."
FIGHT THE "GOOD" FIGHT--
I AM PRETTY SURE THE GOOD FIGHT IS THE ONE AGAINST STATIC CLING
BUT I MIGHT HAVE THE PROTESTANT REFORMATION ALL WRONG.
HOW?
MORALITY HASN'T LEFT THE HOUSE SINCE IT GOT DIGITAL CABLE
AND PRAGMATISM IS PAYING THE BILLS.
BZZZZZZZT
MORALITY

Monoculture's Last Dance

COME ON COME ON COME ON LET ME TELL YOU WHAT IT'S ALL ABOUT
FIGHTING FOR YOUR LIFE INSIDE A THRILLER
THRILLER
TAKE A LOOK AT YOURSELF AND MAKE A CHANGE
DON'T STOP
DON'T STOP 'TIL YOU GET ENOUGH
IF YOU'RE THINKIN' ABOUT MY BABY IT DON'T MATTER IF YOU'RE BLACK OR WHITE
CLICK
SHE SAYS I AM THE ONE
THE CHILD IS NOT MY SON
YOU DON'T EVEN LIKE MICHAEL JACKSON.
I JUST WANT TO BE PART OF SOMETHING.

Any Port in a Storm

IT'S JUST ANOTHER CANON-
JUST ANOTHER HIERARCHY.
I AM OVER THE UNDERGROUND.
BEING SNOBBY ABOUT WHAT MUSIC PEOPLE LIKE OR WHAT KIND OF BIKE THEY RIDE ISN'T ANY BETTER THAN CARING ABOUT WHAT JOBS PEOPLE HAVE OR WHERE THEY WENT TO COLLEGE.
WHAT PART OF JUDGING PEOPLE BY HOW MUCH MONEY THEY DON'T MAKE IS MORALLY SUPERIOR TO JUDGING PEOPLE BY HOW MUCH MONEY THEY DO?
AND WHAT DOES MORALITY HAVE TO DO WITH ANYTHING EXCEPT AS IT'S CONVENIENT?
BEEP BOOP BOOP
CAN WE USE YOUR BATHROOM?

Pyramid Scheme

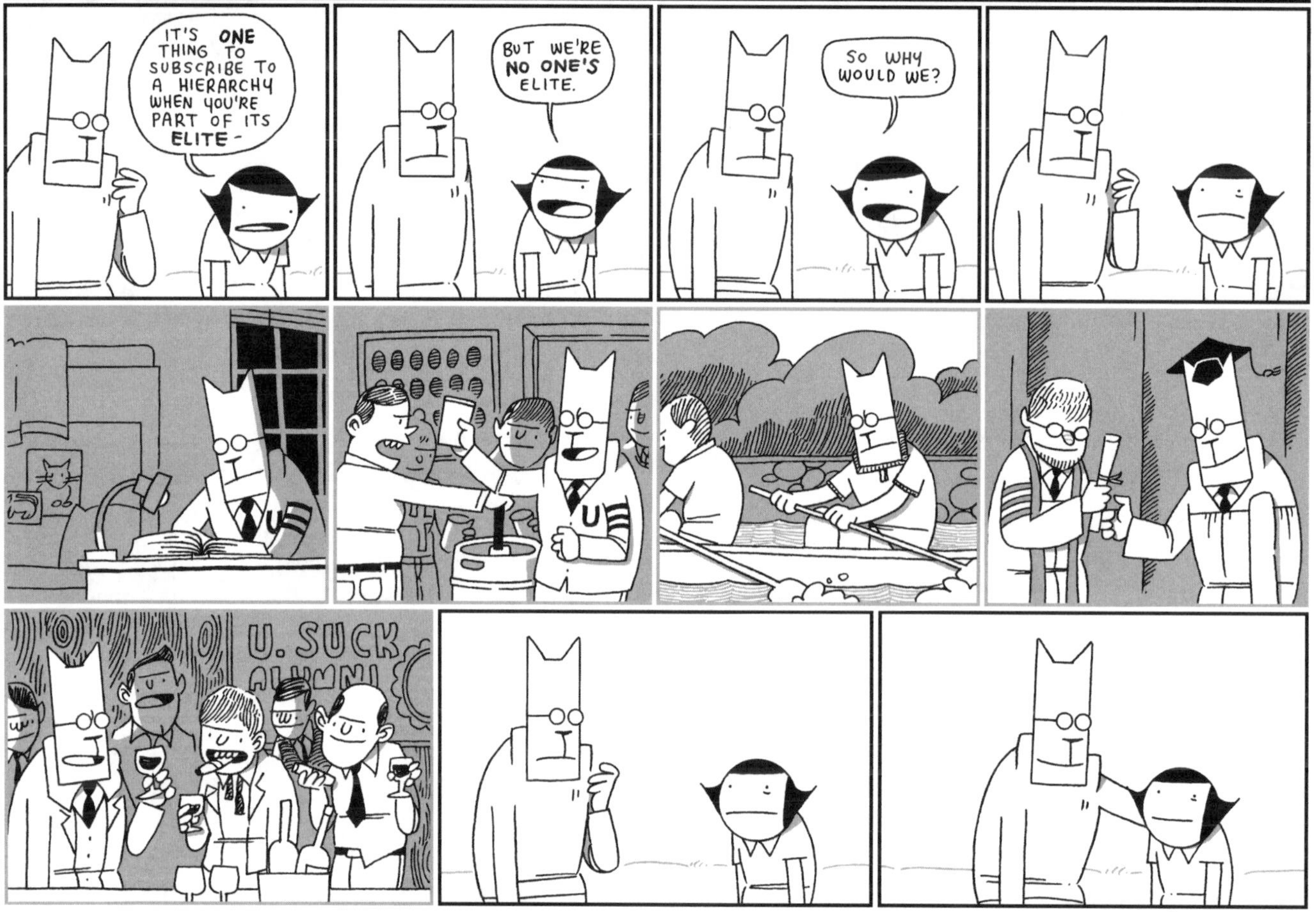
IT'S ONE THING TO SUBSCRIBE TO A HIERARCHY WHEN YOU'RE PART OF ITS ELITE -
BUT WE'RE NO ONE'S ELITE.
SO WHY WOULD WE?
U. SUCK

Simulacra and Simulation

RRING
RRING
RRING
HELLO?
UGH.
WHAT?
THAT RINGTONE.
LET THE DEATH RATTLE OF ANALOG FADE AWAY GRACEFULLY
INSTEAD OF REANIMATING ITS CORPSE FOR A SHAMBLING, MEANINGLESS DIGITAL POST-SCRIPT.
THIS MIGHT BE A WHILE.
DO YOU USE A TYPEWRITER FONT ON YOUR COMPUTER?
MAYBE.
DO YOU BURN MUSIC TO CDs THAT LOOK LIKE LITTLE RECORDS?
WHEN YOU TAKE PHOTOGRAPHS ARE THEY OF COSTUMED BIBLICAL TABLEAUX?
DO YOU RIDE AROUND IN AN AUTOMOBILE WITH A HORSE'S HEAD MOUNTED TO THE FRONT?
OOOoo
YOU'RE USING NEW TECHNOLOGIES TO DO WHAT THEY DO WORST- SIMULATING THE OLD!
AT THIS RATE WE'LL NEVER MAKE IT TO THE FUTURE!
WHAT ARE YOU DOING TONIGHT?

Second Jobs

OTA
TAX
CHK CHK
CHK
RIDDLE
EZ PASS LANE
RIDDLE

Gift Horse

YOUR CHILD'S PHOTOGRAPH TAKEN WITH WIKIPEDIA
AND WHAT ARE **YOU** LOOKING FOR?
QUESTIONS.
QUESTIONS, HUH?
BECAUSE EVERY QUESTION HAS AN ANSWER NOW-
MAYBE LOTS OF ANSWERS, MAYBE ANSWERS THAT ARE UNTRUE.
NO QUESTION IS FOLLOWED BY THAT YAWNING GAP OF NOTHING-
THE BRIEF MOMENT OF SILENCE IN A WORLD FILLED WITH NOISE-
AND AS ANSWERS PROLIFERATE, AS THEY SORT THEMSELVES TOWARD HIGHER DEGREES OF ACCURACY-AT LEAST AS IT IS UNDERSTOOD BY OUR STANDARDS OF TRUTH IN **THIS** SOCIETY,
TODAY-
WHAT'S LEFT BEHIND
ARE THE QUESTIONS.
QUESTIONS WITH NO EXPECTATION OF AN ANSWER-
QUESTIONS FOR THE SAKE OF **WONDER**.
WHAT DID YOU GET?
AN AMERICAN GIRL DOLL.

Karaoke

HE SOLD MORE RECORDS THAN ANYONE ELSE WILL EVER SELL.
HE WAS THE EMBODIMENT OF GLOBAL POP CULTURE.
WAS
WAS THE GUY ON THE COVER OF THRILLER-
IN CAPTAIN EO-
IN PEPSI ADS-
NOW HE'S THE GUY ON THE BOOTLEG TEE SHIRT-
THE GUY ON THE RADIO IN SOMEONE ELSES' CAR-
THE GUY WHOSE NAME IS WRITTEN ON A BEDSHEET AND HUNG OUT A WINDOW-
MJ WE ♡ YOU.
IN DEATH
HE BECAME PART OF OUR FOLK CULTURE
AND THE MESSY PERSONAL LIFE THAT OVERWHELMED HIS POP SUCCESS SUDDENLY MADE A WEIRD KIND OF SENSE.
HE WANTED TO BE A FAIRY TALE AND HE GOT TO BE ONE
BUT YOU CAN'T BE A FAIRY TALE WHILE YOU'RE ALIVE
AND EVERYTHING IS EASIER TO FORGIVE WHEN IT'S OVER.

Death on the Street

!
WHERE HAVE YOU BEEN HIDING?
HI-
NETFLIX.
I MEAN-
I'VE SEEN EVERY EPISODE OF "MAUDE" NOW.
AND
YOU HAVE A PUPPY!
I THOUGHT-
I THOUGHT IF I GOT A DOG I MIGHT MEET MORE PEOPLE.
WHAT ARE THEIR NAMES?
JUDGE
JURY
AND EXECUTIONER.
AND YOU LIVE HERE NOW?
RIGHT ACROSS THE STREET.
I THOUGHT MORALITY LIVED THERE.
OH
NO NO NO
HE MOVED AWAY WITHOUT TELLING ANYONE AGES AGO.
I STILL GET HIS COPIES OF ENTERTAINMENT WEEKLY.

Long Time Listener

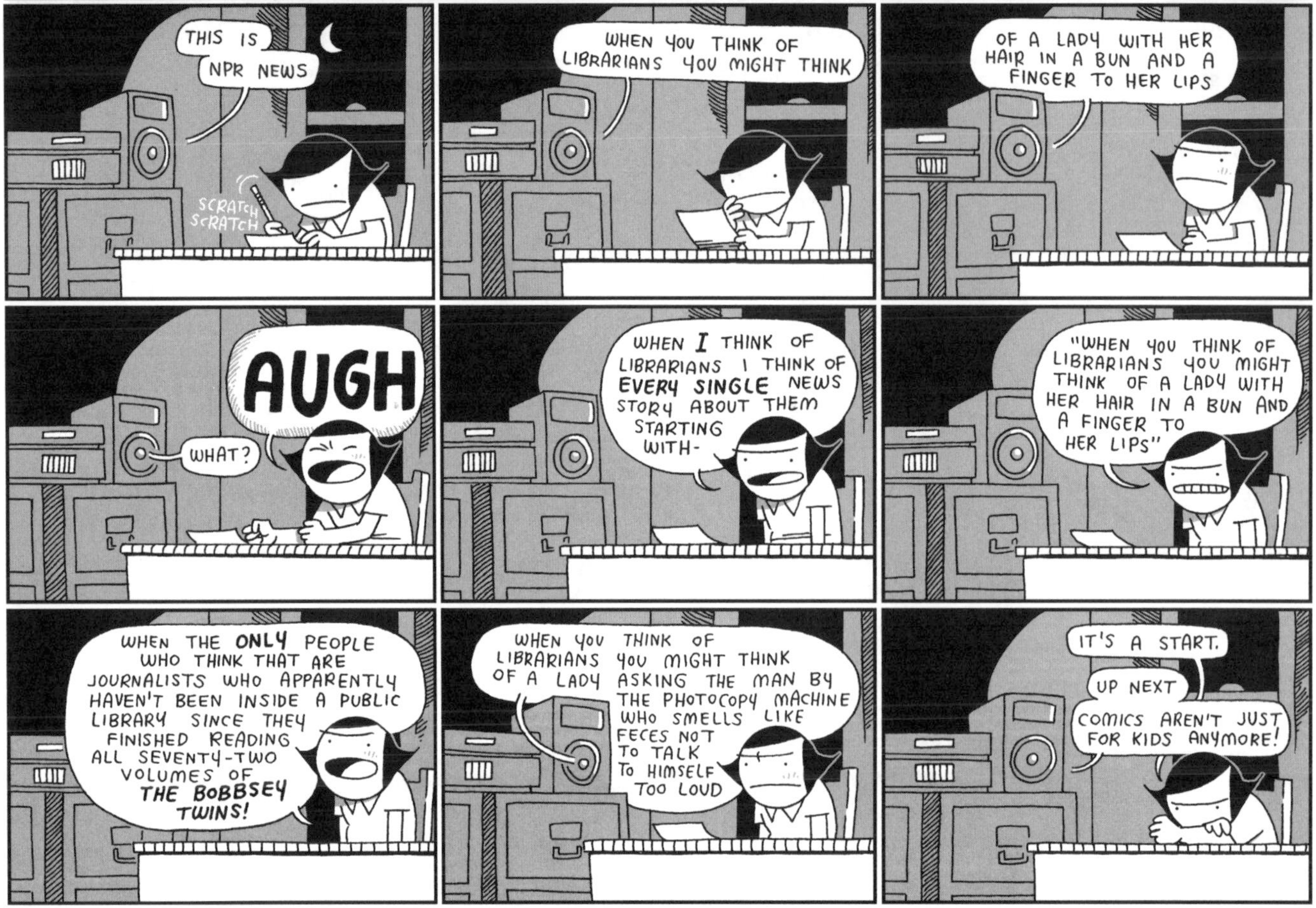
THIS IS NPR NEWS
SCRATCH SCRATCH
WHEN YOU THINK OF LIBRARIANS YOU MIGHT THINK
OF A LADY WITH HER HAIR IN A BUN AND A FINGER TO HER LIPS
AUGH
WHAT?
WHEN I THINK OF LIBRARIANS I THINK OF EVERY SINGLE NEWS STORY ABOUT THEM STARTING WITH-
"WHEN YOU THINK OF LIBRARIANS YOU MIGHT THINK OF A LADY WITH HER HAIR IN A BUN AND A FINGER TO HER LIPS"
WHEN THE ONLY PEOPLE WHO THINK THAT ARE JOURNALISTS WHO APPARENTLY HAVEN'T BEEN INSIDE A PUBLIC LIBRARY SINCE THEY FINISHED READING ALL SEVENTY-TWO VOLUMES OF THE BOBBSEY TWINS!
WHEN YOU THINK OF LIBRARIANS YOU MIGHT THINK OF A LADY ASKING THE MAN BY THE PHOTOCOPY MACHINE WHO SMELLS LIKE FECES NOT TO TALK TO HIMSELF TOO LOUD
IT'S A START.
UP NEXT
COMICS AREN'T JUST FOR KIDS ANYMORE!

What's Important

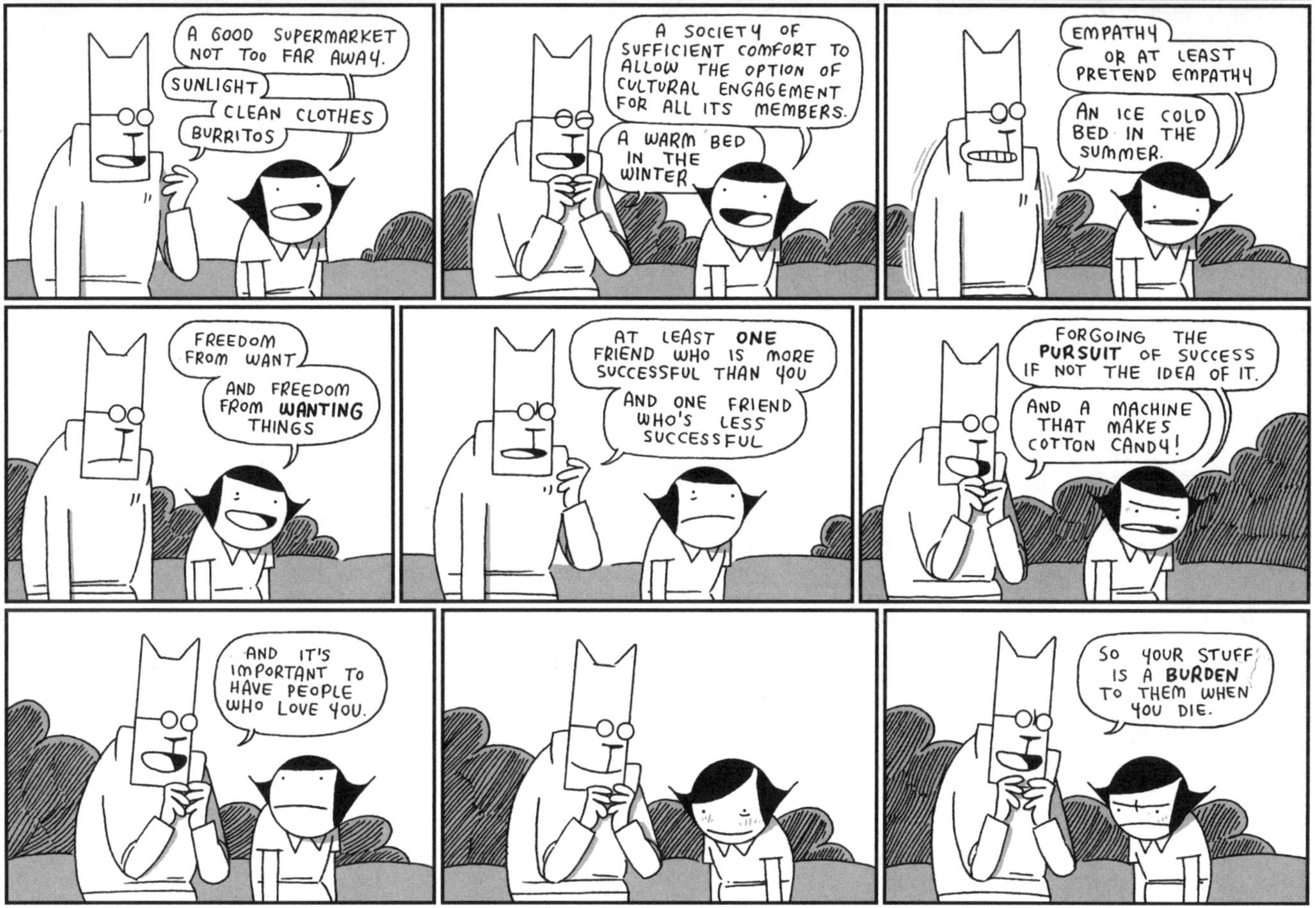

A GOOD SUPERMARKET NOT TOO FAR AWAY.
SUNLIGHT
CLEAN CLOTHES
BURRITOS
A SOCIETY OF SUFFICIENT COMFORT TO ALLOW THE OPTION OF CULTURAL ENGAGEMENT FOR ALL ITS MEMBERS.
A WARM BED IN THE WINTER
EMPATHY
OR AT LEAST PRETEND EMPATHY
AN ICE COLD BED IN THE SUMMER.
FREEDOM FROM WANT
AND FREEDOM FROM WANTING THINGS
AT LEAST ONE FRIEND WHO IS MORE SUCCESSFUL THAN YOU
AND ONE FRIEND WHO'S LESS SUCCESSFUL
FORGOING THE PURSUIT OF SUCCESS IF NOT THE IDEA OF IT.
AND A MACHINE THAT MAKES COTTON CANDY!
AND IT'S IMPORTANT TO HAVE PEOPLE WHO LOVE YOU.
SO YOUR STUFF IS A BURDEN TO THEM WHEN YOU DIE.

Spring Cleaning

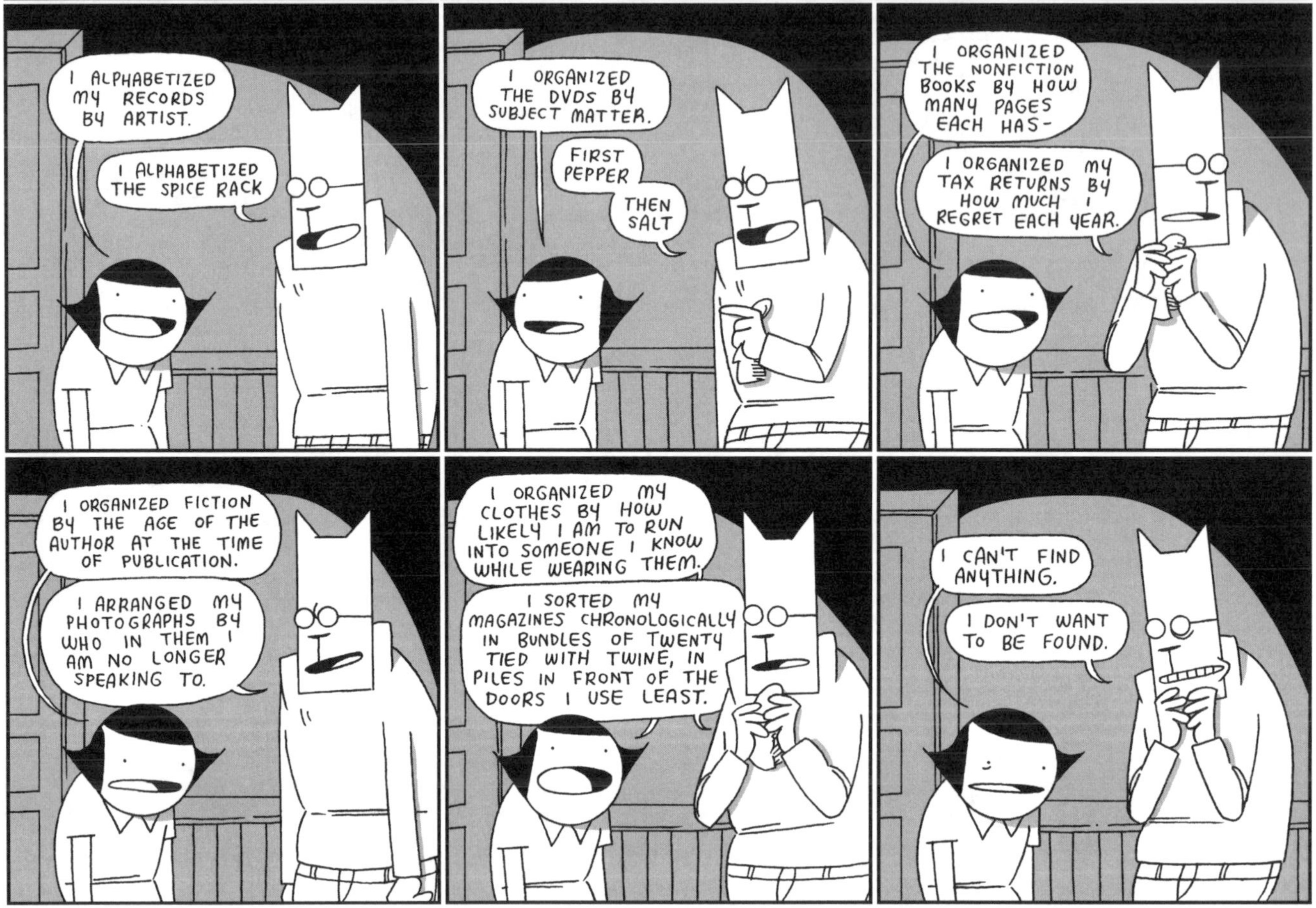
I ALPHABETIZED MY RECORDS BY ARTIST.
I ALPHABETIZED THE SPICE RACK
I ORGANIZED THE DVDS BY SUBJECT MATTER.
FIRST PEPPER
THEN SALT
I ORGANIZED THE NONFICTION BOOKS BY HOW MANY PAGES EACH HAS-
I ORGANIZED MY TAX RETURNS BY HOW MUCH I REGRET EACH YEAR.
I ORGANIZED FICTION BY THE AGE OF THE AUTHOR AT THE TIME OF PUBLICATION.
I ARRANGED MY PHOTOGRAPHS BY WHO IN THEM I AM NO LONGER SPEAKING TO.
I ORGANIZED MY CLOTHES BY HOW LIKELY I AM TO RUN INTO SOMEONE I KNOW WHILE WEARING THEM.
I SORTED MY MAGAZINES CHRONOLOGICALLY IN BUNDLES OF TWENTY TIED WITH TWINE, IN PILES IN FRONT OF THE DOORS I USE LEAST.
I CAN'T FIND ANYTHING.
I DON'T WANT TO BE FOUND.

One Less Place to Visit

WE KNOW PEOPLE MOMENT TO MOMENT.
WE KNOW THEM AS THEIR PRESENT
NOT THE PRESENTS THAT HAVE COME AND GONE.
BUT DEATH TRANSFORMS PEOPLE.
INTO WHAT?
WHEN THEY DIE THEIR LIVES BECOME SOMETHING COMPLETED
A STORY WITH A BEGINNING AND AN END.
A SERIES OF EVENTS BECOMES A TRAJECTORY.
AND LIKE ANY STORY
MOVIE OR BOOK
IT'S ONLY WHEN IT'S OVER
THAT WE CAN START TO SEE WHAT IT MEANT.
THAT THERE'S NO MEANING IN THE PRESENT
ONLY IN THE PAST.
LET'S NEVER GO THERE.

The Call of the Wild

CHEEP
CHEEP
CHEEP
HEY!
THAT BIRD SOUNDS LIKE YOU.
I BEMOAN THE LOSS OF OBSCURITY!
YOU DON'T EVEN REMEMBER OBSCURITY.
NO ONE MISSES WHAT THEY CAN REMEMBER!
VHS
VHS

Summer Plans

ROCK CAMP
CARTOON COLLEGE
THERE'S A SCHOOL FOR EVERYTHING.
WHAT HAPPENED TO THE NOBLE AMATEUR EMERGING FROM THE WOODS WITH THREE CHORDS AND A BURNING MESSAGE?
WHAT SCHOOL TEACHES YOU TO HAVE SOMETHING TO SAY?
DOES EVERYONE HAVE TO BE A PROFESSIONAL?
DO WE NEED A SCHOOL TO LEARN TO WALK - TO EAT - TO TELL STORIES -
DO I NEED A SCHOOL TO WAKE UP IN THE MORNING -
DID YOU GO TO SCHOOL TO LEARN TO BE A CAT?
YES.
YOU SPENT FOUR YEARS LEARNING TO BE A CAT.
TWO
IT'S AN MFA.
WHERE?
IT DOESN'T MATTER WHERE
CAMBRIDGE.

Visions of the Future

LET'S NEVER GET OLD ENOUGH TO TALK ABOUT WHAT WE BELIEVE IN THE LANGUAGE OF TRENDS AND MARKETING.
LET'S NEVER GET OLD ENOUGH TO REALIZE THE THINGS WE BELIEVED IN WERE TRENDS AND MARKETING ALL ALONG.
I DON'T WANT TO MANAGE A CINNABON!

Mantra

WE CAN TAKE THE UPTOWN BUS AND TRANSFER.
SENT FROM MY IPHONE.
I WAS GOING TO TRY TO GET TO THE BEACH BUT IT HASN'T STOPPED RAINING.
SENT FROM MY IPHONE.
SOMEONE TOLD ME THERE'S A GOOD FALAFEL PLACE AROUND HERE.
SENT FROM MY
OK!
YOU **WIN**.
IT MAKES **EVERYTHING** SOUND MORE OBNOXIOUS.
HERE'S THE FIVE DOLLARS.
THANK YOU.
SENT FROM MY IPHONE.
YOU CAN **STOP** NOW.
IT'S KIND OF COMFORTING.

Redundancy Man

LOOK WHAT I MADE!
A PIZZA SLICER.
I INVENTED STONE TOOLS!
I HATE TO BE THE BEARER OF BAD NEWS-
LIAR.
BUT STONE TOOLS WERE INVENTED ABOUT 2.5 MILLION YEARS AGO.
YOU'VE GOT SOMETHING BETTER TO DO?
I WANTED TO GO BIRD-WATCHING ON FRIDAY.
THIS FRIDAY?
OK-
I JUST HAVE TO INVENT A CALENDAR.
USE THE ONE THE MAYANS MADE!
OOOOOOOO WITH THE CHOCOLATES BEHIND THE LITTLE DOORS?

HERE'S THE FIRST.
SSS SIP
SWIZZLE SWIZZLE SWIZZLE
HMM
SWEET
TANGY
UPLIFTING.
IT MAKES ME FEEL BETTER ABOUT MYSELF!
AND THE SECOND.
SWIZZLE SWIZZLE SWIZZLE
FLOWERY
DRY
MY COLON FEELS CLEANSED BUT MY MOUTH FEELS LIKE A CHURCH THREW UP IN IT.
WELL THE FIRST WAS JUSTICE
AND THE SECOND WAS COMPASSION
SO IF YOU HAD TO CHOOSE ONE OR THE OTHER-
WHAT GOES WELL WITH SCOTCH?

ONE BOTTLE OF REGRET!

BAD DECISION DINOSAUR ON THE BOARDWALK

$
DO-NUTS
YOUR PHOTO WITH ABRAHAM LINCOLN

HAM ON A STICK
YOUR PHOTO WITH ABRAHAM LINCOLN

Hunters and Gatherers

EVERYONE'S LOOKING FOR SUCCESS
LIKE IT'S WALDO OR SOMETHING.
BUT WHAT IS SUCCESS?
SOMETHING IN A SANDWICH THAT'S NOT PEANUT BUTTER.
IS IT ALWAYS COMPARATIVE?
A WOOL SWEATER WITH YOUR NAME ON IT.
FOR ME TO SUCCEED
PEOPLE TAKING PICTURES OF YOU
AND YOU DIDN'T JUST FALL DOWN.
DO YOU HAVE TO FAIL?
SAILING YOUR YACHT THROUGH THE ALPS
THE ROPES MADE OF LICORICE
THE SAILS OF PURE SUNSHINE
AND WHEN YOU GO INTO THE SUPERMARKET YOU CAN BUY ANY FRUIT YOU WANT
AND NOT EVEN LOOK AT THE PRICE!
WHY WON'T YOU GET A JOB?

The Searchers

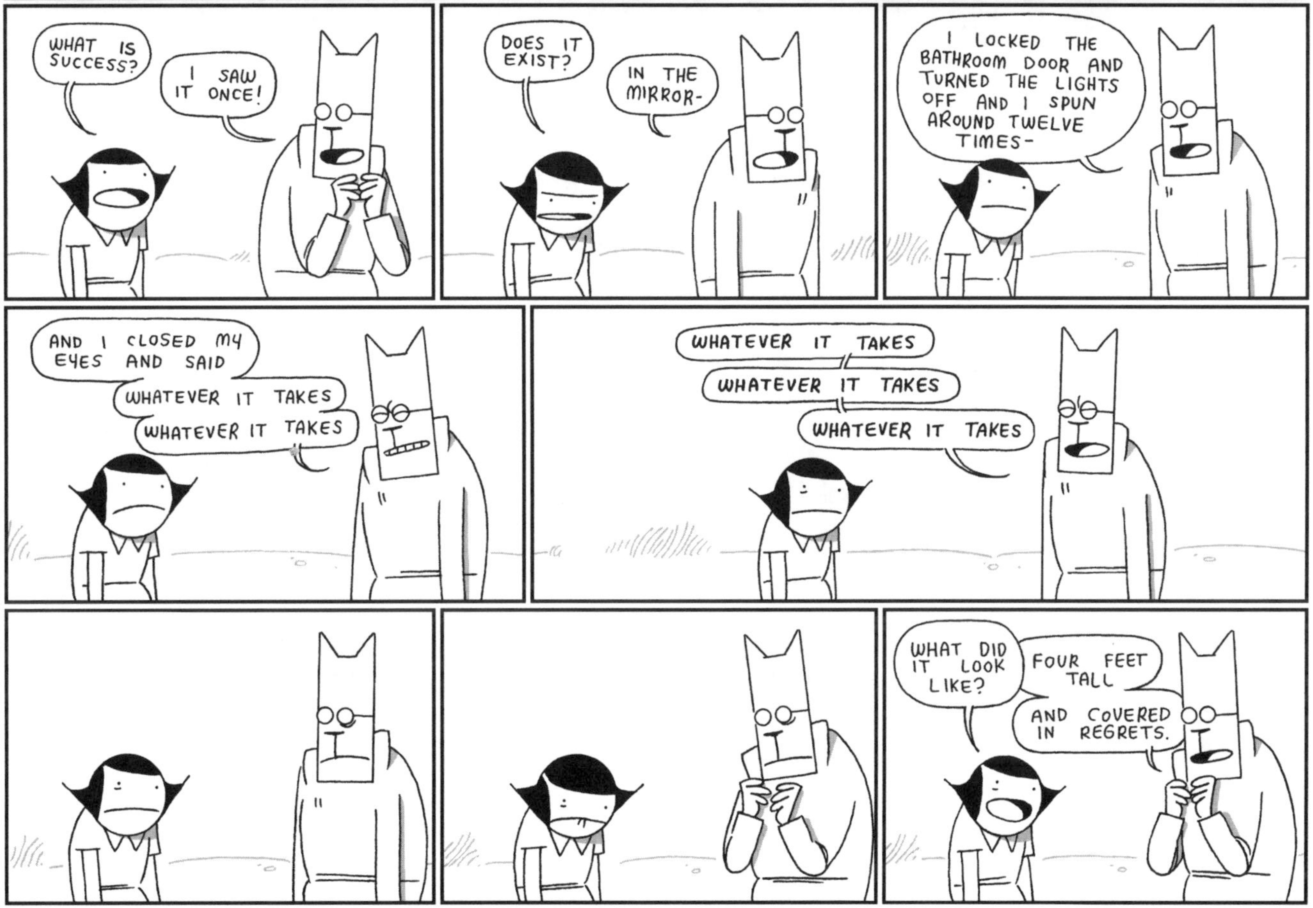
WHAT IS SUCCESS?
I SAW IT ONCE!
DOES IT EXIST?
IN THE MIRROR-
I LOCKED THE BATHROOM DOOR AND TURNED THE LIGHTS OFF AND I SPUN AROUND TWELVE TIMES-
AND I CLOSED MY EYES AND SAID
WHATEVER IT TAKES
WHATEVER IT TAKES
WHATEVER IT TAKES
WHATEVER IT TAKES
WHATEVER IT TAKES
WHAT DID IT LOOK LIKE?
FOUR FEET TALL
AND COVERED IN REGRETS.

And the Band Played On

IF I'M A COG IN SOCIETY'S MACHINE FOR THE MANUFACTURE OF NOTHING
IS MY RESPONSIBILITY TO THE MACHINE
TO FUNCTION TO THE BEST OF MY ABILITY
OR TO STOP FUNCTIONING COMPLETELY.
HOW OLD ARE YOU?
I KNOW STUFF.
BECAUSE YOU'VE GOT
THE SYMPTOMS.
OF WHAT
OF WHAT
I DON'T EVEN WANT TO SAY IT
IT'S BAD NEWS
SICKLE CELL BOHEMIA.
AAAAAAH!

HOLD ON
THAT DOESN'T SOUND SO BAD.
SICKLE CELL BOHEMIA IS **TOTALLY OK** AS LONG AS YOU GET IT OUT OF YOUR SYSTEM IN YOUR TWENTIES.
AFTER THAT THE DISEASE BECOMES **DISFIGURING**
DOING **LONG-TERM DAMAGE** TO YOUR ABILITY TO OWN NICE THINGS.
IF YOU MANAGE TO MAKE IT TO YOUR MID-THIRTIES WITH SICKLE CELL BOHEMIA-
YOU'RE A SURVIVOR.
YOU'RE A **LOSER**.
THERE ISN'T A CURE?
THE CURE'S **WORSE**.

Dog Days

THERE IS ONE WEEK A YEAR
WHEN ANYTHING THAT FALLS
HITS THE GROUND
WITHOUT MAKING A SOUND.
WHEN EVERYTHING IS A REPEAT
EVEN THE NEWS
AND EVERYONE IS ON VACATION EXCEPT FOR YOU.
GAS

Ain't No Sanity Clause

MAVIS
BEACON
I ALWAYS THOUGHT SHE WAS A REAL PERSON.
SOMEONE WHO HAD FOUGHT HER WAY UP IN THE WORLD WITH HER **INCREDIBLE** TYPING SKILLS.
BUYING BUSINESS CLOTHES AT DAFFY'S
PRETENDING YOU'RE NOT EATING LUNCH BECAUSE YOU'RE BUSY
GOING HOME TO A SHARE IN WASHINGTON HEIGHTS WITH TWO GIRLS WHO WORK IN P.R. - AND THEY ARE **ALWAYS** ON THE FUTON WATCHING WHATEVER TV SHOW YOU DON'T WANT TO SEE -
THEN YOU TEACH A FEW SMALL CLASSES
THE KIDS OF THE GUY IN CHARGE OF 5 1/4" DISC PRODUCTION COME IN -
BEFORE YOU KNOW IT YOU'RE ON YOUR PRIVATE PLANE DIVE-BOMBING GRACELAND BECAUSE HOW FAST COULD **THAT** GUY TYPE?
NOSTALGIA MAKES FOOLS OF US ALL
AND SOME OF US RICH.
I'M STILL WAITING.

The Game of Life

YOUR WHOLE FAMILY COMES TO YOUR BAR MITZVAH!
COLLECT 500 DOLLARS.
GET A JOB YOU HATE.
TELL YOURSELF IT'S TEMPORARY.
LOSE ONE TURN.
THIS GAME ISN'T ANYTHING LIKE LIFE.
YOU JUST DON'T LIKE LOSING.
IN THE NAVY
EAT COLD SPAGETTIOS OUT OF THE CAN.
STRIKE UP A CONVERSATION AT THE BUS STOP.
MAKE A FRIEND!
I DON'T GET MONEY FOR THAT?
THANK YOU FOR YOUR YEARS OF SERVICE.
ENJOY THE TENNESSEE ERNIE FORD RETIREMENT PLAN.
DEATH AT A RIPE OLD AGE!
THE WHOLE TOWN CRIES AS YOUR BODY IS SET ABLAZE AND SENT OUT TO SEA.
SO NOW WE FIGURE OUT WHOSE LIFE IS WORTH MORE?
WE ADD UP OUR MONEY - OUR FRIENDS, AND OUR FAMILY -
AND MULTIPLY BY ZERO.
I WIN!

On Digital Photography

DO YOU REMEMBER PHOTOGRAPHS?
LIKE ON FACEBOOK?
PHOTOGRAPHS
THE IMAGE TURNED OBJECT
I THINK I SAW THAT IN A MOVIE ONCE.
AND WHEN WE HELD THIS OBJECT IN OUR HANDS AND LOOKED OUT AT THE WORLD-
I HOLD PICTURES IN MY HANDS ALL THE TIME.
IT STOPPED BEING BIG AND SCARY AND INCOMPREHENSIBLE AND BECAME A SOURCE OF IMAGES
IMAGES TO BE COLLECTED.
JUST TODAY I HELD A SUPERMARKET CIRCULAR
AND THOSE OBJECTS WE MADE OF THE WORLD WERE PUT IN ALBUMS OR STORED IN SHOE BOXES OR PRINTED IN MAGAZINES
AN AD FOR A TYLER PERRY MOVIE
PHYSICAL JUNK IN A JUNK SOCIETY-
AND A PICTURE OF SOMEONE'S LOST PUPPY.
UNTIL DIGITAL PHOTOGRAPHY-
WHEN THE REPRODUCTION OF PHOTOGRAPHIC IMAGES WAS LIBERATED FROM THE OBJECT!
AND PHOTOGRAPHS BECAME INFORMATION JUNK.
I SHOULD HAVE KEPT THAT PUPPY.

PHOTOGRAPHY IS COMMODIFIED SEEING.
WHEN WE PHOTOGRAPH OURSELVES INDULGING IN LEISURE
THAT LEISURE IS IN SERVICE OF CREATING A PRODUCT
AN IMAGE
SO THAT EVEN OUR LEISURE TIME CAN BE CALLED PRODUCTIVE.
TO WIELD A CAMERA-
SNICKER
WHAT?
NO ONE TAKES PICTURES WITH A CAMERA ANY MORE.
PHOTOGRAPHY IS THE MOST MODERN OF ART FORMS!
WHO'S SEEN THE MODERN WORLD AROUND LATELY?
ANYONE?
OR DID A STACK OF NEWSPAPERS FALL AND BURY HIM IN HIS HOME?
WE WERE GOING TO MEET YESTERDAY
AT JOHNNY ROCKETS
BUT HE WAS JUMPED BY SOME LOCAVORES.

THE PHOTOGRAPH CAPTURED A MOMENT-
ELEVATED THAT MOMENT BY DEEMING IT WORTHY OF CAPTURE-
BACK WHEN PHOTOGRAPHY WAS BOUND BY THE FINITE LIMITS OF CHEMICAL REACTIONS-
I HOPE THE MOMENT GOT AWAY.
BACK IN A WORLD WHERE A WAR COULD BE UNDERSTOOD AS A PHOTOGRAPH OF SIX MEN RAISING A FLAG.
BUT THE WORLD HAS FIRED THE WEDDING PHOTOGRAPHER AND PUT DIGITAL CAMERAS ON ALL THE TABLES AT THE RECEPTION
AND WE UNDERSTAND THE TRUTH AS SOMETHING NOT FIXED IN PLACE BY ONE PERSON
BUT SOMETHING BUILT OF MANY ACCOUNTS BY MANY PEOPLE AND LIVING IN THE SPACES BETWEEN THEM.
AND WHILE THE CONSTANT FLOW OF DIGITAL IMAGES HAS ITS OWN MEANING
THE INDIVIDUAL IMAGE HAS NONE.

PHOTOGRAPHS CAPTURE THE DISAPPEARING WORLD
SO THEY BECOME MORE INTERESTING AS THEY AGE
AND AS THEY DEVELOP THE PATINA OF AGE.
I KNOW WHAT YOU'RE GOING TO SAY-
YOU DO?
"DIGITAL PHOTOGRAPHS DON'T HAVE A PATINA!"
I WAS?
WE JUST HAVEN'T LEARNED TO SEE IT YET.
BUT THEY WILL
THEY WILL
THEY WILL
TO BE PHOTOGRAPHED IS TO EXIST.
TO BE PHOTOGRAPHED IS TO BE BEAUTIFUL FOREVER.
OR DRUNK AT A PARTY FOREVER.
SOME CALL IT HEAVEN.

WHEN WE BEGAN TO DOCUMENT THE WORLD
WITH DRAWINGS AND MAPS AND
SHEET MUSIC
AND PHOTOGRAPHS
WE DOCUMENTED BRIEF MOMENTS PULLED WITH GREAT EFFORT FROM TIME'S SLIPSTREAM
THERE HE IS!
NOW OUR VIEW OF ANY INDIVIDUAL MOMENT IS OBSCURED BY THE ARMIES OF DOCUMENTS CREATED TO MEMORIALIZE IT.
-WINK
PHOTOGRAPHS TAKEN TO CAPTURE IT-
AND BOOKS WRITTEN TO UNDERSTAND IT.
"IN THE REAL WORLD SOMETHING **IS** HAPPENING, AND NO ONE KNOWS WHAT IS GOING TO HAPPEN.
IN THE IMAGE-WORLD IT HAS HAPPENED, AND WILL FOREVER HAPPEN THAT WAY."
DAMMIT.

Great Escapes

OOOOOOOH!
SARDINES.
IT'S EMPTY?
THEY COULDN'T HAVE GONE FAR.
THE RIVER!
IMAGINE SPENDING MONTHS IN A DARK AND WET LITTLE ROOM PACKED WITH STRANGERS.
AND NOW
THEY'RE FREE
WATCH OUT FOR THE SEAGULL!
I COULD LIVE IN HERE.
IT'S NOT MUCH BUT IT'S HOME.

Escalator to Success

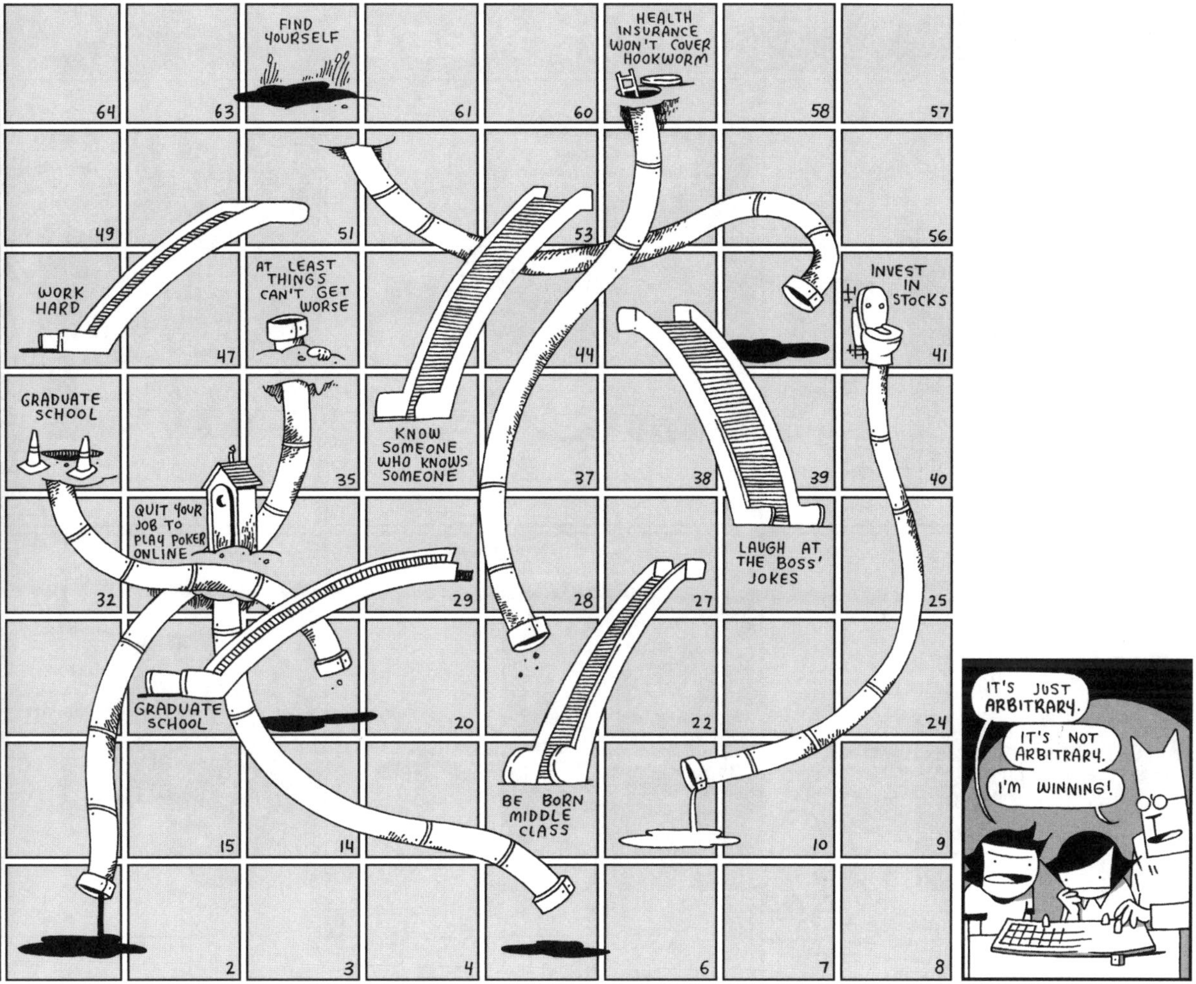
FIND YOURSELF
HEALTH INSURANCE WON'T COVER HOOKWORM
64
63
61
60
58
57
49
51
53
56
WORK HARD
AT LEAST THINGS CAN'T GET WORSE
INVEST IN STOCKS
47
44
41
GRADUATE SCHOOL
KNOW SOMEONE WHO KNOWS SOMEONE
35
37
38
39
40
QUIT YOUR JOB TO PLAY POKER ONLINE
LAUGH AT THE BOSS' JOKES
32
29
28
27
25
GRADUATE SCHOOL
20
22
24
BE BORN MIDDLE CLASS
15
14
10
9
2
3
4
6
7
8
IT'S JUST ARBITRARY.
IT'S NOT ARBITRARY.
I'M WINNING!

Value Menu

Protect me from what I want
I FIGURE
THERE ARE THREE KINDS OF PEOPLE
Protect me from what I want
PEOPLE WHO DON'T GET ENOUGH TO EAT
PEOPLE WHO GET DIABETES
Protect me from what I want
AND PEOPLE WHO HAVE TROUBLE FALLING ASLEEP.
Protect me from what I want
I NEED TO MAKE ENOUGH MONEY TO BE IN THAT **LAST** GROUP.
Protect me from what I want
Protect me from what I want
YOU KNOW MONEY WON'T MAKE YOU HAPPY.
IT SURE MAKES BEING UNHAPPY EASIER.

Birnam Wood

WE'RE LOST IN THE FOG OF INFORMATION.
IT'S NOT FOGGY.
IT'S A METAPHOR.
AND WE'RE LOST IN A FOREST.
STUPID GOOGLE MAPS.
THE LIBRARY OF ALEXANDRIA CONTAINED ALL THE KNOWLEDGE OF THE ANCIENT WORLD
AND NOW WE HAVE-
IT'S CALLED A PHONE.
DOES IT TELL YOU HOW TO LIVE?
WHAT TRUTH MEANS?
HOLD ON-
NO.
BUT I CAN TELL YOU HOW KINGS QUEST IV ENDED.
MAYBE.
ALL THE INFORMATION IN THE WORLD AND HALF OF IT'S WRONG.
AND THE ANCIENT WORLD WAS BETTER?
HAVE FUN WITH ALCHEMY.
I CAN STILL TURN UNEMPLOYMENT INTO AN IPHONE APP!

Sharing

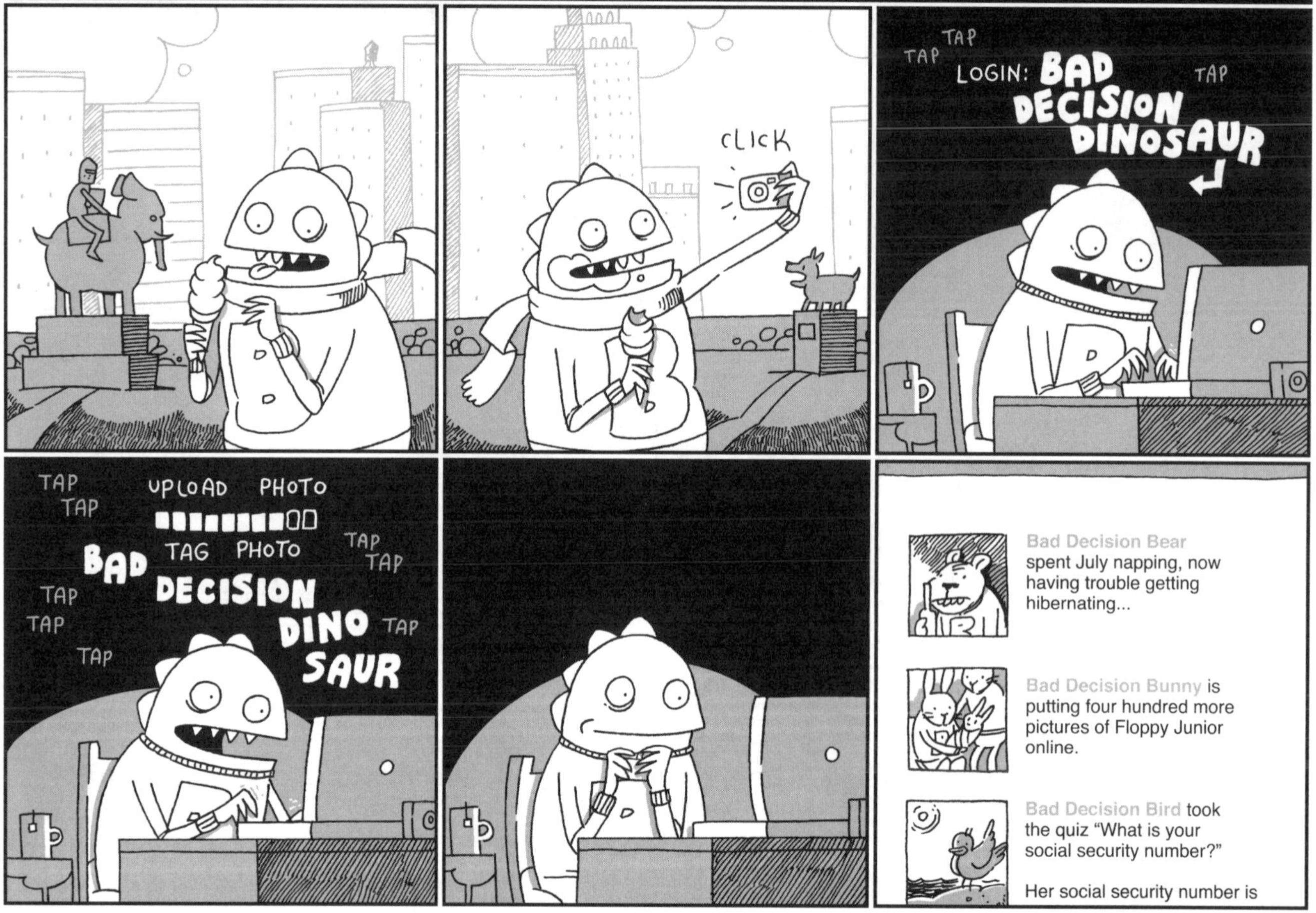

CLICK
TAP TAP
LOGIN: BAD DECISION DINOSAUR ↵
TAP
TAP TAP
UPLOAD PHOTO
TAG PHOTO
BAD DECISION DINO SAUR
TAP TAP
TAP TAP
TAP
TAP
Bad Decision Bear spent July napping, now having trouble getting hibernating...
Bad Decision Bunny is putting four hundred more pictures of Floppy Junior online.
Bad Decision Bird took the quiz "What is your social security number?"
Her social security number is

Secular Humanists

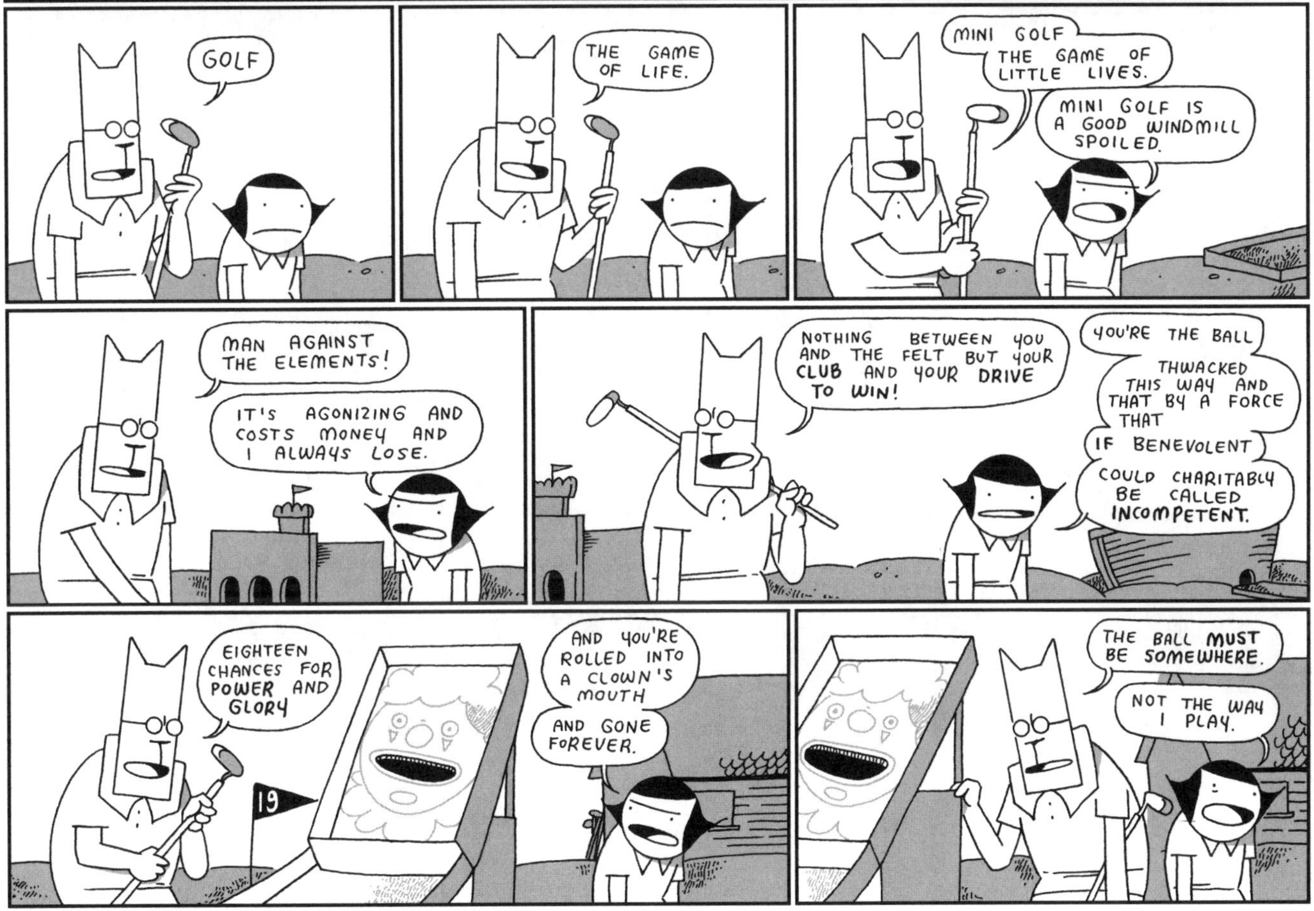

GOLF
THE GAME OF LIFE.
MINI GOLF
THE GAME OF LITTLE LIVES.
MINI GOLF IS A GOOD WINDMILL SPOILED.
MAN AGAINST THE ELEMENTS!
IT'S AGONIZING AND COSTS MONEY AND I ALWAYS LOSE.
NOTHING BETWEEN YOU AND THE FELT BUT YOUR CLUB AND YOUR DRIVE TO WIN!
YOU'RE THE BALL
THWACKED THIS WAY AND THAT BY A FORCE THAT
IF BENEVOLENT
COULD CHARITABLY BE CALLED INCOMPETENT.
EIGHTEEN CHANCES FOR POWER AND GLORY
19
AND YOU'RE ROLLED INTO A CLOWN'S MOUTH
AND GONE FOREVER.
THE BALL MUST BE SOMEWHERE.
NOT THE WAY I PLAY.

On Safari

SSSSSSHH
WHAT ARE WE LOOKING FOR?
INSPIRATION.
THAT'S A TOUGH NUT.
SSSSSSHH!
WHEN I WAS SMALL
WE'D GO HUNTING FOR HO-HOS
ALL YOU NEEDED WAS A DING-DONG AND A NET.
CLICK
THE TRAP!
INSPIRATION?
CONSISTENCY.
WHO DOESN'T LIKE A HOBGOBLIN?

Borderline

WE'RE GOING FOR A RIDE!
I'LL NEED A DRINK.
I'LL GET SNACKS!
WHERE ARE WE GOING?
UP-
IN THE SKY WHERE
CLOUDS
. . .
YOU CAN'T DRIVE LIKE THIS.
PFFFFF
AND I CAN'T DRIVE WHILE TEX MEXING.
IT'S DANGEROUS!
A LITTLE VIHUELA NEVER HURT ANYONE.
AND WHY DO WE DRIVE IN A PARKWAY
AND CRY IN A DRIVEWAY?
MOTHER
I'm SORRY
BOO HOO HOO

J. Crüe
WHY THE SUDDEN MAINSTREAM CULTURAL INTEREST
IN A CAPPELLA GROUPS AND SHOW CHOIRS?
MAYBE AFTER THE HEADY RUSH OF CHEAP CONSUMER PRODUCTS, MY SUPER SWEET 16, VARIABLE RATE MORTGAGES ON CHEAPLY BUILT HOMES WITH TWO STORY FOYERS AND AN OBSESSION WITH THE NOUVEAU RICHE
AMERICA IS READY TO SETTLE DOWN WITH THE GOOD OLD UPPER MIDDLE CLASS.
I DON'T WANT TO LIVE IN THAT WORLD.
AND IT DOESN'T WANT YOU.

Do It Yourselfers

!
I FOUND A BOOK IN THE GARBAGE!
I GOT MOVIES!
"HAVE A NICE DAY."
CHRISTMAS 1988.
"CAPTAIN SAD AND HIS SHIP OF FOOLS."
A UKULELE WITH NO STRINGS!
"MONSTER IN LAW."
UNO!
I CAN'T WAIT TO GET HOME!
BAP BAP BAP
WE CAN ADD THESE TO THE CANON.
THE CANON?
BIP
THE CANON I'VE BEEN BUILDING IN THE BASEMENT.
I THOUGHT WE WERE BUILDING A BONFIRE.

A Town Called Euphemism

PASSED AWAY.
LEFT THE BUILDING.
KICKED THE BUCKET
BOUGHT THE FARM
RESTRUCTURING.
REDUNDANCIES.
LADIES' ROOM.
FRATERNAL ORDER
LISTENER SUPPORTED
SOCIAL NETWORKS
INTERESTING.
ENLISTING WORDS TO OBSCURE THE TRUTH
OBSCURING THE TRUTH IS ONE OF SOCIETY'S MAIN OBJECTIVES
OR WE MIGHT REALIZE HOW LITTLE IT'S ALL WORTH
AND THEN WHO WOULD SHOW UP TO WORK ON TIME?
I WANT MY FARM AND MY BUCKET BACK.

Last Call
EVERY DAY AT EIGHT PM
SINCE 1928
A BUGLEMAN HAS SOUNDED LAST POST AT YPRES
IN REMEMBRANCE OF THE SOLDIERS WHO DIED THERE IN THE FIRST WORLD WAR
A WAR THAT ENDED IN 1918.
WHAT WERE THEY DOING FOR TEN YEARS?
CLIPPING COUPONS?
WE NEED TO FORGET THINGS BEFORE WE WANT TO REMEMBER THEM.
SO FLANNEL IS BACK.
I WAS GOING TO SAY.

Available Everywhere

GUG GUG GUG
GUG GUG
GUG GUG GUG
SLOOOORP
AH
TSSSSH
THAT'S THE FIFTH CAN YOU'VE HAD OF-
MR. PIB.
DOCTOR THUNDER?
DOCTOR NO HEALTH INSURANCE.
IT SOUNDS LIKE SOMETHING I'D LIKE.
YOU WIN FREE SHOES WITH EVERY DIABETES.
HOW MANY CALORIES DOES IT HAVE?
"NEVER YOU MIND."

Noise Complainer

BANG BANG BANG
CUT IT OUT!
HEY MOM.
HEY STANLEY.
WANT SOME CAKE?

Self-Made Up

KHALIL GIBRAN.
VANILLA ICE.
I WOULD-
WHAT GAME IS THIS?
KHALIL GIBRAN
MOVED FROM POVERTY IN OTTOMAN SYRIA TO POVERTY IN BOSTON IN 1895
BUT HE CLAIMED TO BE OF ROYAL ANCESTRY.
VANILLA ICE GREW UP IN MIDDLE CLASS SOUTH FLORIDA
BUT HIS 1991 AUTHORIZED BIOGRAPHY CLAIMS HE GREW UP IN A MIAMI GHETTO.
WE ALL LIKE TO PRETEND!
IN AN AMERICA THAT CONSIDERED ITSELF AN OLIGARCHY
BIRTH IS WHAT YOU ARE
I LIKE TO PRETEND THAT I LIVE IN THE MALL.
IN A SELF-STYLED MERITOCRACY
YOU ARE HOW FAR YOU'VE COME.
I SLEEP IN THE MATTRESS STORE
THE TRUTH DOESN'T CHANGE
BUT THE LIES DO.
AND EAT ALL THE SOFT PRETZELS I CAN CARRY.
I WANT TO LIVE IN A LIGHTHOUSE.

The White Mountains

YOU'VE GOT TO LIE LOW ONCE MATURITY HITS.
STICK YOUR HEAD OUT OF THE PARAPET AND-
BAM!
THEY FLATTEN YOU INTO THE GROUND
MAINTAINING THE GLOSSY SMOOTH SURFACE OF CIVILIZATION.
ONE MINUTE YOU ARE WHOLELY YOURSELF
THE NEXT YOU ARE A COMPROMISE BETWEEN YOUR TRUE SELF AND WHAT YOU WANT FROM THE WORLD
AND WHAT THE WORLD WANTS FROM YOU.
SO YOU HIT A CERTAIN AGE AND THEN YOU HAVE TO SUBSUME YOUR NEEDS TO THE NEEDS OF SOCIETY?
YES!
WHY DOES THAT NOT STRIKE ME AS A BAD THING?
WHOSE SIDE ARE YOU ON?

A Shotglass in the Dark

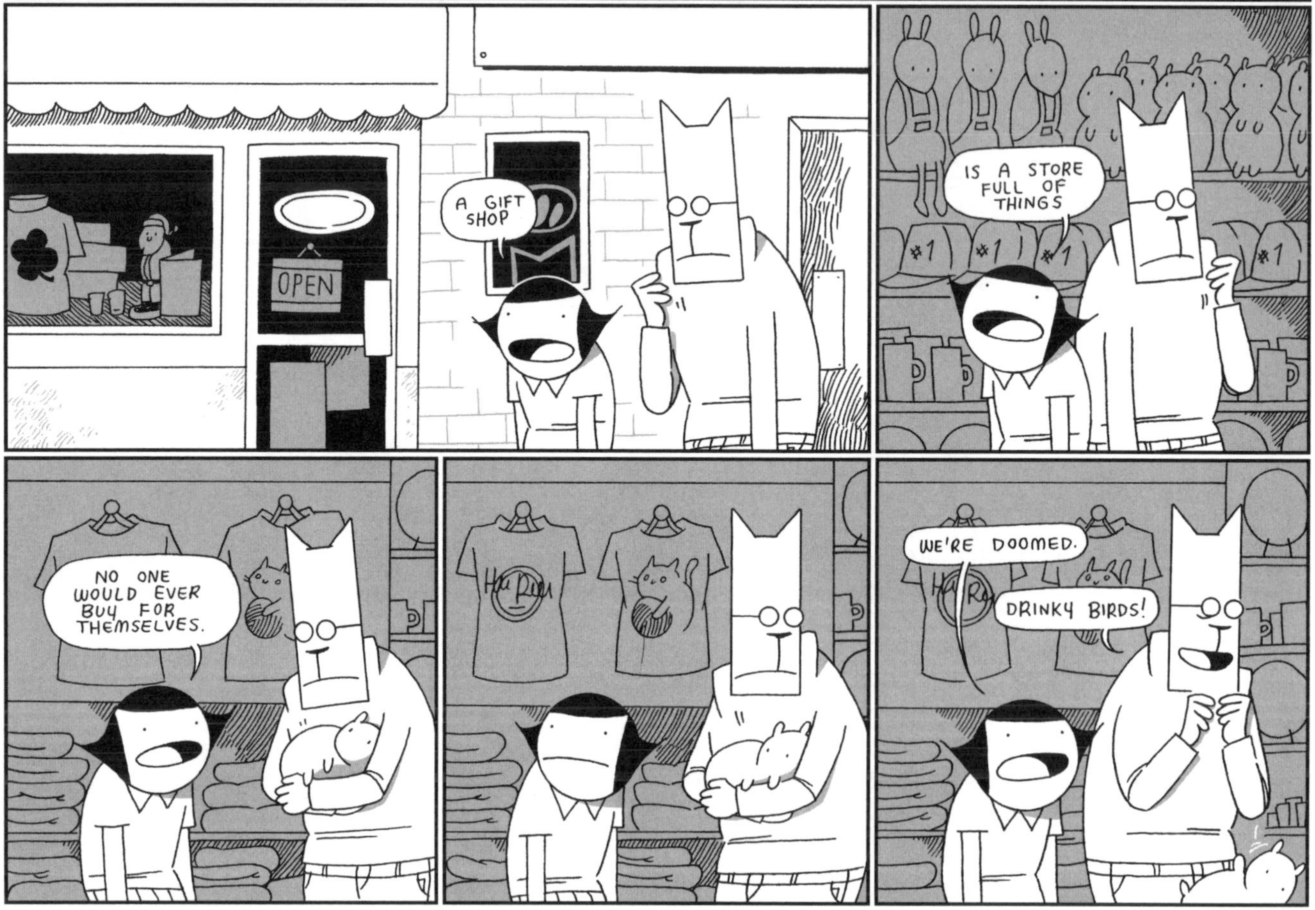
OPEN
A GIFT SHOP
IS A STORE FULL OF THINGS
#1
NO ONE WOULD EVER BUY FOR THEMSELVES.
WE'RE DOOMED.
DRINKY BIRDS!

Higher Ground

IF OUR LIVES ARE THAT BRIEF MOMENT OF TRANSIT
FROM NOTHING
AND BACK TO NOTHING AGAIN
GOOD INTENTIONS ARE WORTHLESS.
GOOD DEEDS TOO–
MONEY DOESN'T MATTER.
FRIENDS DON'T MATTER.
SUCCESS IS MEANINGLESS.
EVEN FAILURE IS MEANINGLESS.
IS THE ONLY PURPOSE OF OUR SHORT STEP FROM THE VOID
TO GRANT US THE AWARENESS OF ALL THAT NOTHING?
OR IS THERE A WORLD ABOVE THE CLOUDS?
I'VE BEEN THERE!
IT'S COVERED IN BIRD CRAP.

CCTV

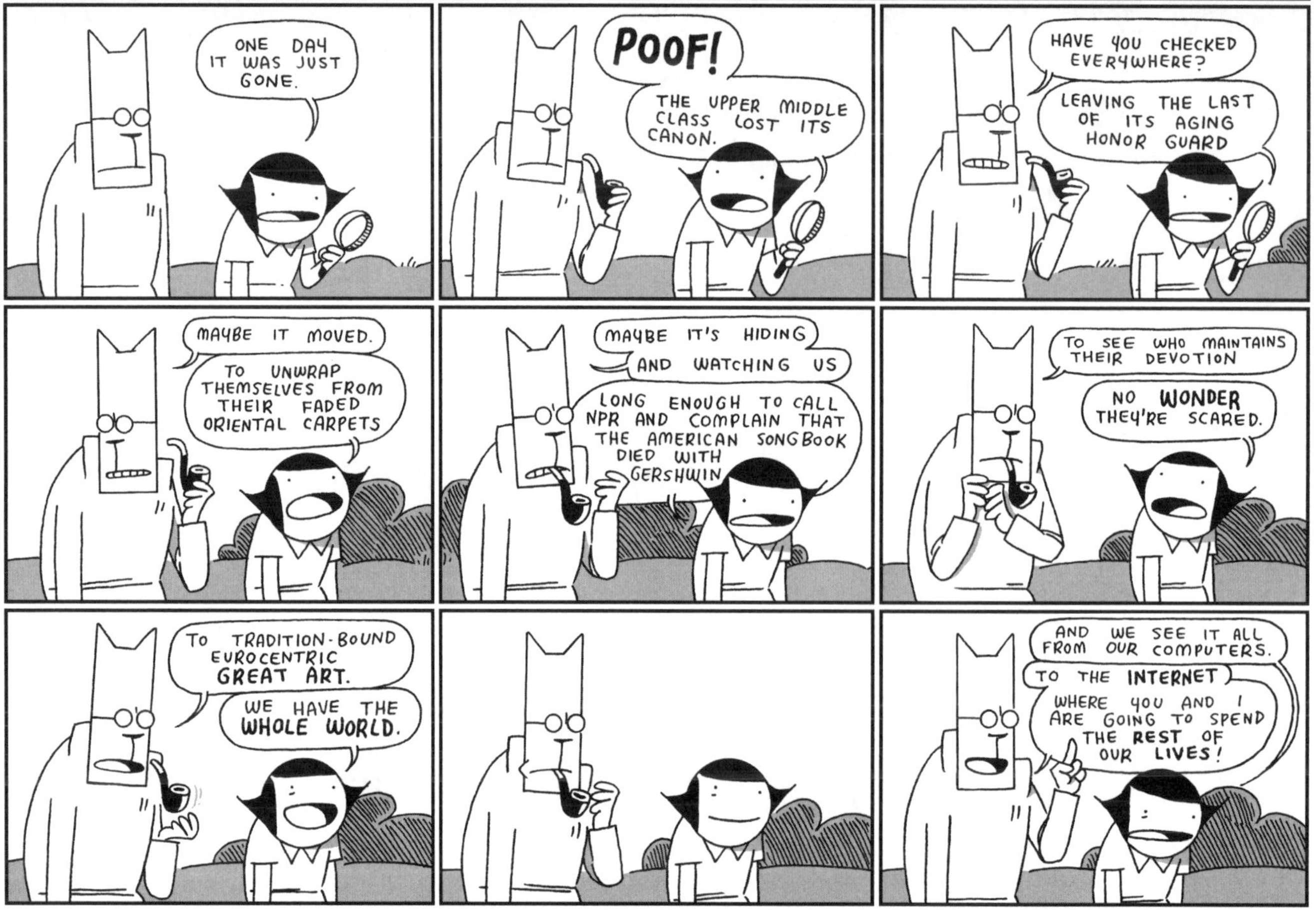
ONE DAY IT WAS JUST GONE.
POOF!
THE UPPER MIDDLE CLASS LOST ITS CANON.
HAVE YOU CHECKED EVERYWHERE?
LEAVING THE LAST OF ITS AGING HONOR GUARD
MAYBE IT MOVED.
TO UNWRAP THEMSELVES FROM THEIR FADED ORIENTAL CARPETS
MAYBE IT'S HIDING
AND WATCHING US
LONG ENOUGH TO CALL NPR AND COMPLAIN THAT THE AMERICAN SONGBOOK DIED WITH GERSHWIN
TO SEE WHO MAINTAINS THEIR DEVOTION
NO WONDER THEY'RE SCARED.
TO TRADITION-BOUND EUROCENTRIC GREAT ART.
WE HAVE THE WHOLE WORLD.
AND WE SEE IT ALL FROM OUR COMPUTERS.
TO THE INTERNET
WHERE YOU AND I ARE GOING TO SPEND THE REST OF OUR LIVES!

Small Pleasures

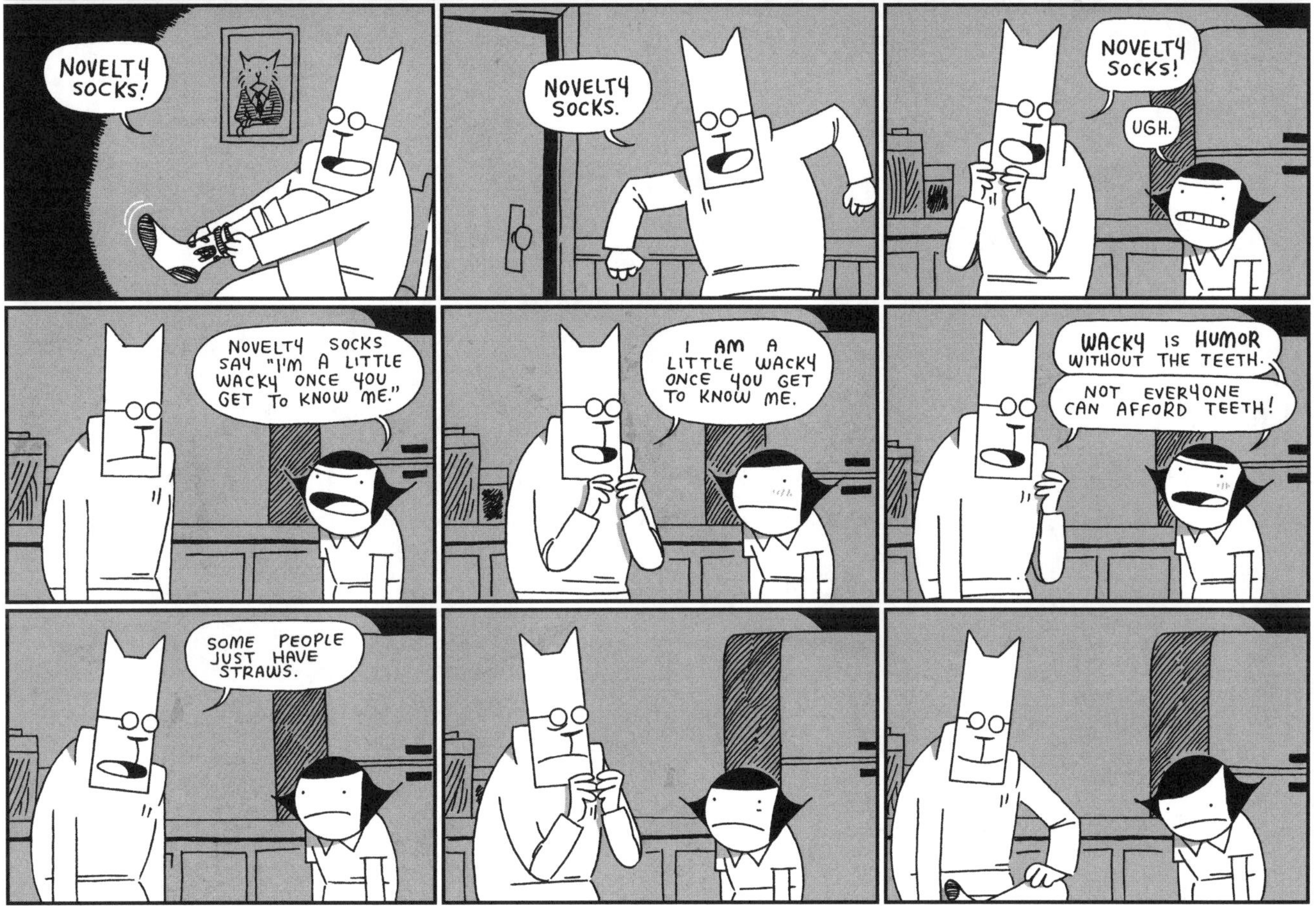
NOVELTY SOCKS!
NOVELTY SOCKS.
NOVELTY SOCKS!
UGH.
NOVELTY SOCKS SAY "I'M A LITTLE WACKY ONCE YOU GET TO KNOW ME."
I AM A LITTLE WACKY ONCE YOU GET TO KNOW ME.
WACKY IS HUMOR WITHOUT THE TEETH.
NOT EVERYONE CAN AFFORD TEETH!
SOME PEOPLE JUST HAVE STRAWS.

Bed Time Theories

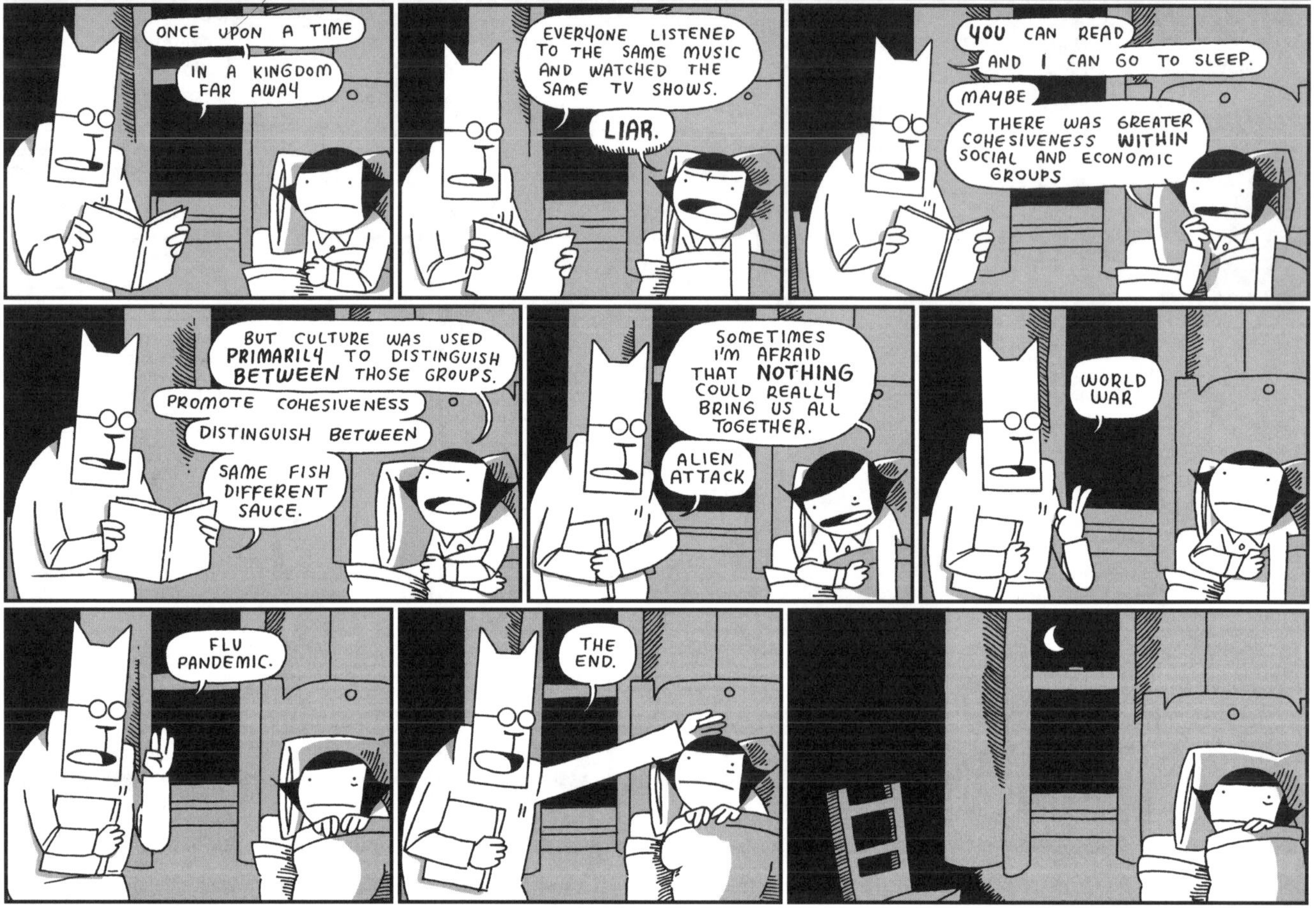
ONCE UPON A TIME
IN A KINGDOM FAR AWAY
EVERYONE LISTENED TO THE SAME MUSIC AND WATCHED THE SAME TV SHOWS.
LIAR.
YOU CAN READ
AND I CAN GO TO SLEEP.
MAYBE
THERE WAS GREATER COHESIVENESS WITHIN SOCIAL AND ECONOMIC GROUPS
BUT CULTURE WAS USED PRIMARILY TO DISTINGUISH BETWEEN THOSE GROUPS.
PROMOTE COHESIVENESS
DISTINGUISH BETWEEN
SAME FISH DIFFERENT SAUCE.
SOMETIMES I'M AFRAID THAT NOTHING COULD REALLY BRING US ALL TOGETHER.
ALIEN ATTACK
WORLD WAR
FLU PANDEMIC.
THE END.

Are Friends Elastic?

Bop
Bop
Bop
Bop
Bop
BOP
BOP
WHY AREN'T WE CHANGING?
INTO WHAT?
BOP
BOP
I DON'T KNOW
SOME NEWER VERSION OF OURSELVES
I HAVE A BLAZER!
Bop
Bop
SOCIETY DEMANDS AN ABILITY TO SHIFT FROM PERSONA TO PERSONA
AND A STRAW HAT
AND A RACCOON COAT
SNAP
BUT WHAT IF ONE PERSONA IS ALL I CAN DO?
AWOoooOOOOOOOOoo

Old Friends

DING DONG
I'M DARK SECRET, AND THIS IS-
THE SHAME.
YOU FOUND ME
SLAM
IT'S HALLOWEEN!
IT IS?

HELP ME

The Doomed Voyage

THE USUAL?
THE USUAL?
THE USUAL?
YOU DON'T KNOW ME
AND YES
THIS HASN'T BEEN A YEAR
IT'S EXHAUSTING
JUST ONE DAY
365 TIMES
TO EXPERIENCE EVERYTHING ANEW EVERY DAY
I AM GOING TO GET ON MY BOAT AND SAIL WHERE THE WIND TAKES ME
WHILE KEEPING TRACK OF STUFF LIKE YOUR ZIP PLUS FOUR
AND WHEN I HIT LAND
I WILL WALK UNTIL I FIND A TOWN WHERE
MOUSTACHES ARE SINCERE - AND BEARDS ARE IRONIC-
AND I WILL PLANT MY OAR IN THE GROUND AND SAY
MY NEW LIFE STARTS HERE.
YOU DON'T HAVE A BOAT.
GET OUT.

PADDLE PADDLE PADDLE
KICK KICK KICK
ADVENTURE
MFF
PADDLE PADDLE
LIFE WITHOUT THE NUMBING EFFECTS OF
KICK KICK
ROUTINE
RUMBLE
SPLASH
UP RETROSPECTOSCOPE!
MAYBE THINGS WEREN'T SO BAD.

Z
Z
Z
MMMMMRGH
DO I KNOW YOU?
WE WENT TO COLLEGE TOGETHER.
I LIVE IN YOUR NEIGHBORHOOD.
WE MET AT A PARTY.
I'M STEVE'S FRIEND!
I'M HIS COUSIN.
OH GOD
DO YOU WANT TO SEE PICTURES OF MY BABY?
IT'S MY SOCIAL NETWORK
UNTIE ME
WHERE WOULD YOU GO?

SAW SAW SAW
SAW SAW SAW SAW SAW SAW
C'MON
C'MON
OH THIS COULD BE EASIER.
STUPID-
SAW SAW SAW
SWISS ARMY SPOON
I **HAD** TO BE DIFFERENT
PLINK
BUT IT SURE CAME IN HANDY DURING THAT JELLO STORM.

SNAP
DID I LEAVE THE OVEN ON?

HF HF HF HF
WHEEZE
WHEEZE
WHEEZE
Entering
METAPHOR CITY
PLOP!
Entering
METAPHOR CITY
Entering
METAPHOR CITY

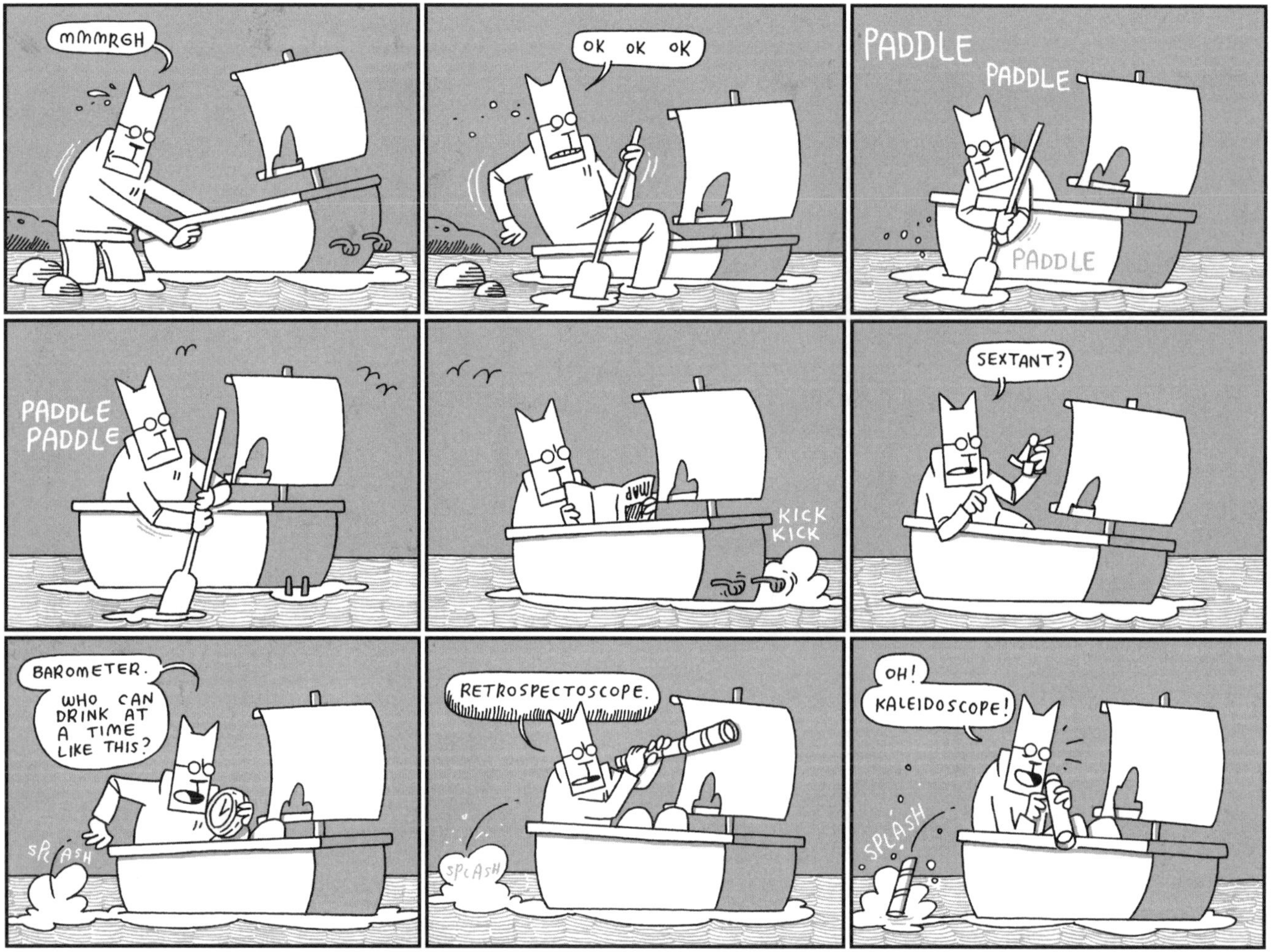
MMMRGH
OK OK OK
PADDLE
PADDLE
PADDLE
PADDLE
PADDLE
MAP
KICK
KICK
SEXTANT?
BAROMETER.
WHO CAN DRINK AT A TIME LIKE THIS?
SPLASH
RETROSPECTOSCOPE.
SPLASH
OH!
KALEIDOSCOPE!
SPLASH

Z Z Z
STOP
DON'T LOOK AT ME
YOUR ROPES FEEL LIKE TINY HUGS
HOME
I WILL MAKE HOT COCOA
AND TURN OFF ALL THE LIGHTS
UNPLUG ALL THE APPLIANCES
AND LUXURIATE
IN BEING UNWATCHED AND UNHEARD.
SURPRISE!

IT'S NOT MY BIRTHDAY.
THAT'S WHY IT'S A SURPRISE.
THE UNKNOWN IS NOT MY FRIEND.
YES IT IS!
HE **REMEMBERED**!
BAM!
THAT WAS FROM THE UNKNOWN?
THAT WAS FROM ROBERT GOBER
THE UNKNOWN SENT A FRUIT PLATE.

Surrounded

WE CAN'T CREATE OBJECTS WITH MEANING-
MEANING IS NOT INHERENT IN THINGS.
WE CREATE MEANING FOR THE OBJECTS AROUND US
TO MAKE SENSE OF THE WORLD.
THEN WHY BOTHER MAKING ANYTHING?
ALL THAT TIME-
I COULD HAVE GROWN TOMATOES.
I COULD HAVE BRUSHED MY TEETH FIVE TIMES A DAY.
I WOULD HAVE SUCH CLEAN TEETH!
BUT
IF WE CAN'T CREATE OBJECTS TO COMMUNICATE OUR SPECIFIC INTENTIONS-
WE CAN CREATE THINGS THAT ATTRACT MEANING
LIKE A BEAR TRAP!
LIKE A BIRD FEEDER.
TO ATTRACT THE MEANING OTHER PEOPLE CREATE IN THE WORLD
AND COLLECT IT AROUND US
AND HOLD IT CLOSE.

Everyone Says

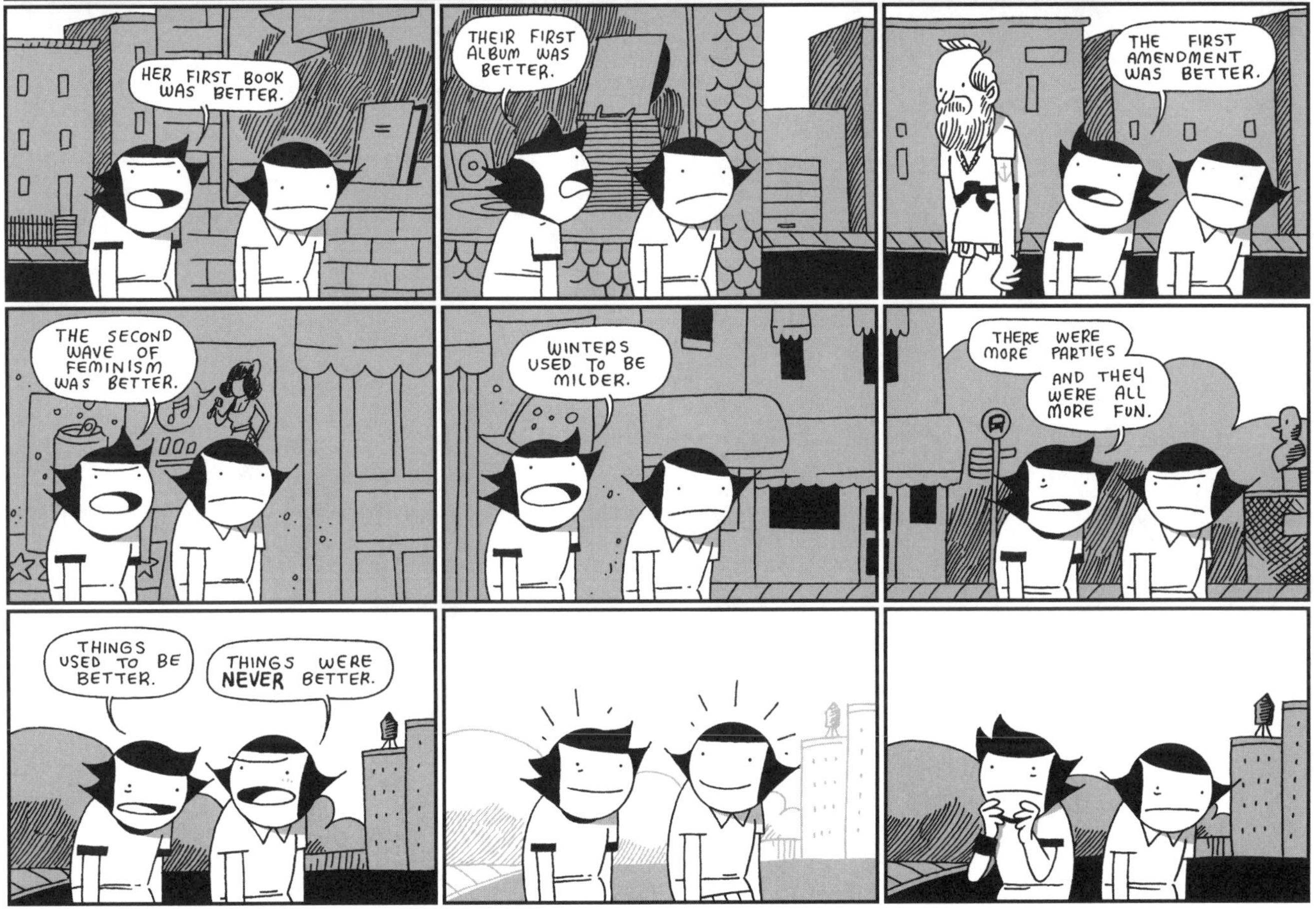

HER FIRST BOOK WAS BETTER.
THEIR FIRST ALBUM WAS BETTER.
THE FIRST AMENDMENT WAS BETTER.
THE SECOND WAVE OF FEMINISM WAS BETTER.
WINTERS USED TO BE MILDER.
THERE WERE MORE PARTIES
AND THEY WERE ALL MORE FUN.
THINGS USED TO BE BETTER.
THINGS WERE **NEVER** BETTER.

Bargain Hunters

WHY CAN'T WE DO SOMETHING FOR THE SAKE OF DOING IT?
WHY DOES THERE ALWAYS HAVE TO BE A PERSONAL ADVANTAGE AT THE END OF THE RAINBOW?
PFFF
THAT'S NOT WHAT'S AT THE END OF THE RAINBOW.
THEN WHAT IS
AN ESTATE SALE.
AUTHENTICITY IS
STRIP-MINING OTHER PEOPLES' HISTORY.
THE DEAD DON'T CARE.
GARBAGE IS FOR THE LIVING.
TO THE VICTOR GO THE SPOILS
AND LIVING IS VICTORY ENOUGH.
EVERYTHING'S FULL OF MEANING WHEN YOU DON'T UNDERSTAND IT!

Bait and Switch

I HAD A DREAM
THAT MY ACTIONS WERE DRIVEN BY A UNIQUE PERSONALITY
AND THEN I WOKE UP
AND REALIZED
IT WAS JUST A PERSONA
NOT AN AUTHENTIC EXPRESSION OF SELF
AHEM
BUT A COLLECTION OF HABITS DESIGNED TO DISTRACT THE WORLD FROM WHAT I FEAR I REALLY AM.
TAP TAP
JINGLE JINGLE JINGLE
A DIME FOR THE AUTHENTICITY JAR.
"AUTHENTIC EXPRESSION OF SELF"?
THAT'S AT LEAST A QUARTER.

authenticity is...
... six people sharing one bathroom.
authenticity is...
...wearing your winter coat at home.
authenticity is...
... pooling change for beer.
uthenticity is...
... a consolation prize.
authentici
... other peoples' childhoods.
authenticity is...
... haircuts with nail scissors.
authenticity is...
... living in one place forever.
thenticity is...
... street furniture.
enticity is...
I HOPE NO ONE ELSE SPEAKS ENGLISH HERE
... when no one else speaks English.
authent
... obsolete technologies.
ticity is...
... obsolete hobbies.
ity is...
... chickens.

authenticity is...
... the industrial district, two years before you got there.
authenticity is...
... music coming out of cars.
uthenticity is...
... having so many exciting things to do that you just stay home.
authenticity is...
... dog racing.
aut
SCRATCH SCRATCH
... pestilence.
authenticity is...
POKE
$
$
... street crime.
authenticity is...
... other peoples' problems.
authenticity is...
... wearing underpants at the beach.
uthenticity is...
... not much fun.
authenticity is...
... memories of the missing versus the existence of the refurbished.
y is...
... the easiest way to add value to low culture products.
authenticity is...
... holding the opinions you are expected to have.

Just Desserts

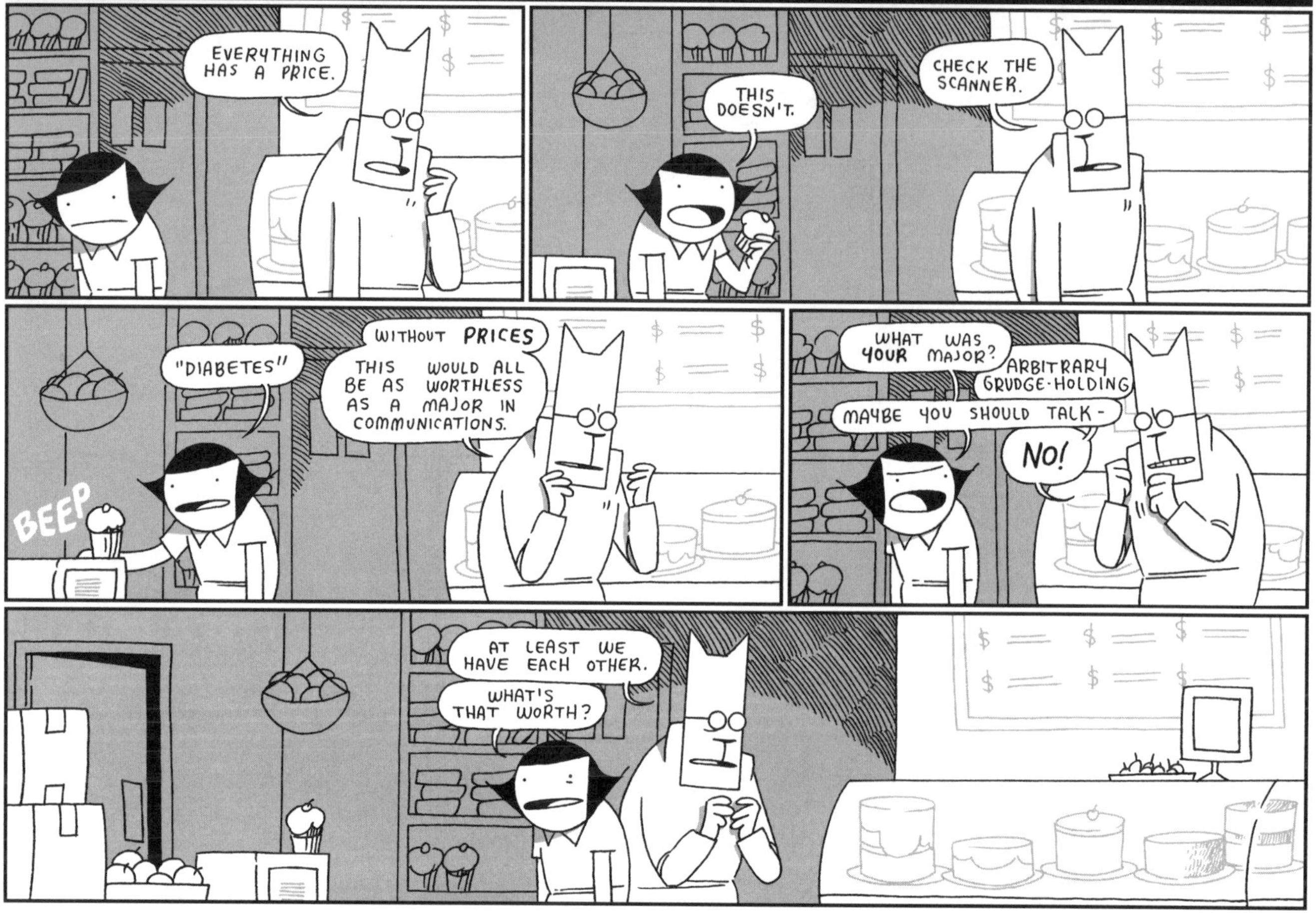

EVERYTHING HAS A PRICE.
THIS DOESN'T.
CHECK THE SCANNER.
BEEP
"DIABETES"
WITHOUT PRICES THIS WOULD ALL BE AS WORTHLESS AS A MAJOR IN COMMUNICATIONS.
WHAT WAS YOUR MAJOR?
ARBITRARY GRUDGE-HOLDING
MAYBE YOU SHOULD TALK-
NO!
AT LEAST WE HAVE EACH OTHER.
WHAT'S THAT WORTH?

The Old Hag

I WAKE UP UNABLE TO BREATHE
I CAN SEE
BUT I CAN'T CALL OUT
I TRY TO GET UP BUT A HEAVY PRESSURE HOLDS ME DOWN AND
MY EVERY ATTEMPT AT MOVEMENT REINFORCES THE REALITY OF MY SITUATION-
I'M TRAPPED.
I GET THE SAME THING.
THEN IT'S REAL?
AND COMMONLY KNOWN AS
WAKING UP IN THE MORNING TO GO TO WORK.
I DON'T HAVE A JOB.
YOU'RE SICK.

2009 BC

THE CLOSE OF ANOTHER YEAR.
YOU KNOW WHAT THAT MEANS-
THE DAYS ARE AT THEIR SHORTEST.
FOOD BECOMES SCARCE.
IT'S TIME TO LOOK BACK ON THE BEST OF 2009 BC!
AHEM
THE WHEEL
SIMPLE TOOLS
BATHING
CARLSBAD CAVERNS
YOU'VE BEEN?
HOW IS IT?
DARK.
LADY GAGA
LADY GAGA SOUNDS LIKE THE ARCHAEOPTERYX BY THE MARSH!
LADY GAGA IS MAKING A METACULTURAL CRITIQUE OF THE ARCHAEOPTERYX BY THE MARSH.
I REALLY LIKE THE CAFE THAT OPENED UP BY THE LIMESTONE DEPOSIT.
THE ETHNIC PLACE?
THE ONE THAT COOKS EVERYTHING WITH
WITH
FIRE?
IT'S DIFFERENT
I DON'T SEE HOW YOU COULD EAT THAT EVERY DAY.
I REMEMBER WHEN ALL THIS NEIGHBORHOOD HAD WAS THE CARRION PIT AND A KFC.
THE YEARS JUST FLY BY.

Followed

SOMETIMES
I'M AFRAID THAT I'M BEING WATCHED.
BUT WHEN I-
LOOK BACK!
THERE'S NO ONE THERE.
JUST LITTLE SIGNS-
A SNAPPED TWIG
A CIGARETTE BUTT
A TWEET
BEING TAGGED IN A PHOTO OR
MENTIONED IN A STATUS UPDATE.
A PASSING COMMENT ON THE BLOG OF SOMEONE I DON'T KNOW-
MY WORDS AND ACTIONS
TAKEN OUT OF CONTEXT
TO MAKE SOMEONE ELSES' POINT.
I AM NOT YOUR RAW MATERIAL!
AND
SOMETIMES
I'M AFRAID NO ONE IS WATCHING.

Miracle Workers

A TELEPHONE BOOTH IN THE DESERT.
PEOPLE USED TO GET EXCITED ABOUT THIS STUFF
DRIVING OUT HERE JUST TO WAIT FOR IT TO RING.
RING
HELLO?
WHY?
BECAUSE IT'S NOWHERE
WHERE IS NOWHERE NOW?
INSIDE US ALL.

IT'S A BAD DECISION HOLIDAY

DING
DING
DING
DING
DING
DING
DING
DING
DING
YOU'RE VOLUNTEERING!
THAT'S SO COOL.
ARE YOU COLLECTING MONEY?
TEETH
DING
DING
DING

PLOP
KNOCK
KNOCK
KNOCK

YOU THINK YOU CAN COME BACK AND BE THE GOOD GUY
YOU'RE NOT THE GOOD GUY
YOU'RE THE GUY WHO TOOK OFF WHEN POP GOT SICK
I HAD AN OFFER
TO MANAGE A CIRCUIT CITY
MOM TURNED YOUR ROOM INTO A FREIGHT ELEVATOR.

Chicken of the Sea

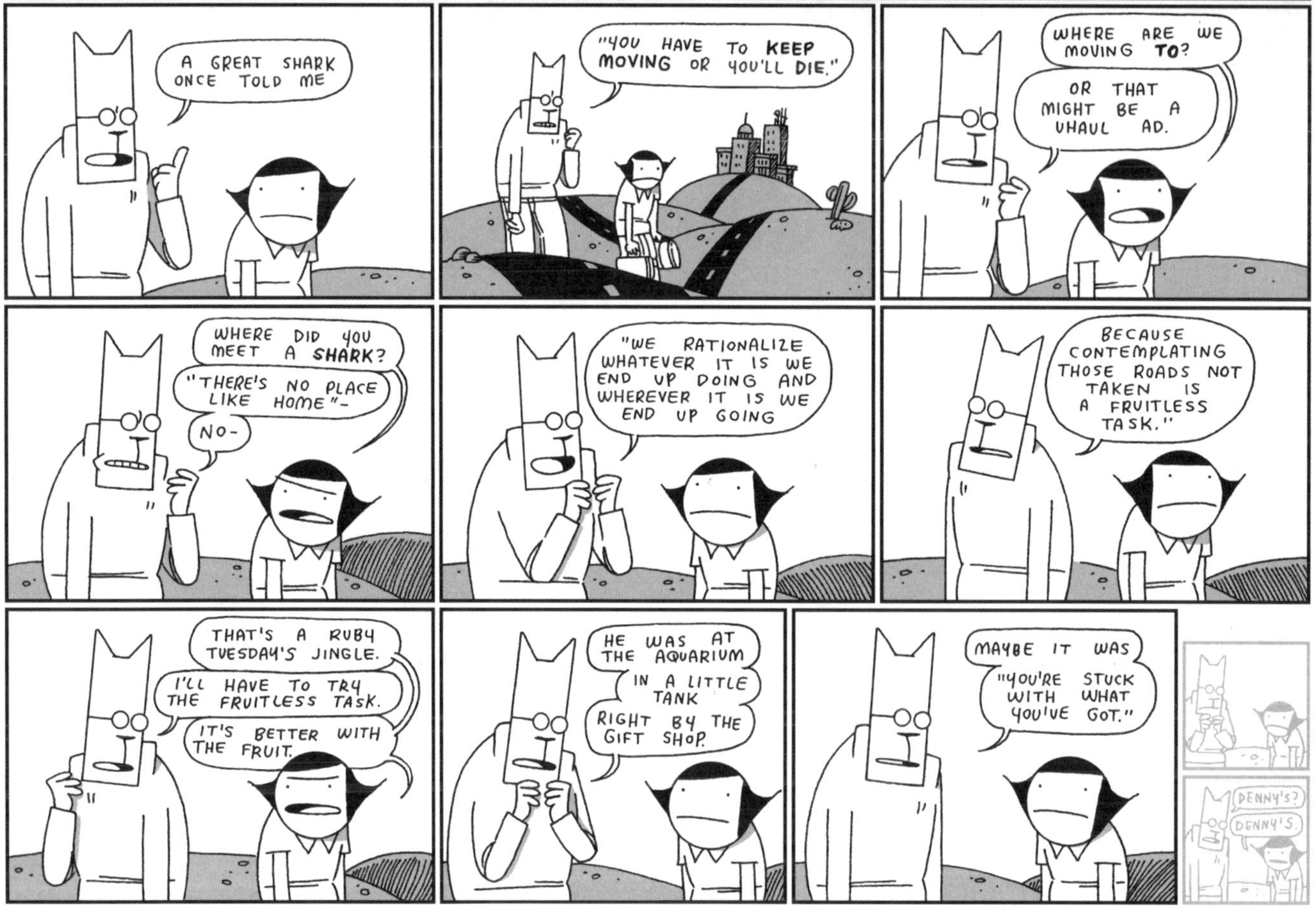

A GREAT SHARK ONCE TOLD ME
"YOU HAVE TO KEEP MOVING OR YOU'LL DIE."
WHERE ARE WE MOVING TO?
OR THAT MIGHT BE A UHAUL AD.
WHERE DID YOU MEET A SHARK?
"THERE'S NO PLACE LIKE HOME"-
NO-
"WE RATIONALIZE WHATEVER IT IS WE END UP DOING AND WHEREVER IT IS WE END UP GOING
BECAUSE CONTEMPLATING THOSE ROADS NOT TAKEN IS A FRUITLESS TASK."
THAT'S A RUBY TUESDAY'S JINGLE.
I'LL HAVE TO TRY THE FRUITLESS TASK.
IT'S BETTER WITH THE FRUIT.
HE WAS AT THE AQUARIUM
IN A LITTLE TANK
RIGHT BY THE GIFT SHOP.
MAYBE IT WAS
"YOU'RE STUCK WITH WHAT YOU'VE GOT."
DENNY'S?
DENNY'S.

End Times

LOOKING BACK
IT'S EASY TO MISTAKE PROXIMITY FOR FATE.

About the Author